MENDI[P]

Limestone Quarryi[ng]

A CONFLICT OF INTEREST

Edited by
Frank Raymond

Somerset Books

First Published in 1994 by Somerset Books

ISBN 0 86183 266 3

British Library Cataloguing-in-Publication Data
CIP data for this book is available from the British Library

SOMERSET BOOKS
Official publisher to
Somerset County Council
Halsgrove House
Lower Moor Way
Tiverton
EX16 6SS

0884 243242
0884 243325

Printed and bound in Great Britain
by Longdunn Press Ltd., Bristol

CONTENTS

Record of Proceedings of a Seminar held on 23 October 1993 to Examine the Dilemma facing Mendip

Jointly organised by
The Royal Bath & West of England Society and
The Royal Geographical Society (Western Region)

The contribution made by **National Westminster Bank plc** is gratefully acknowledged, without whose support it would not have been possible to produce this publication.

FOREWORD

The subject of limestone quarrying is a sensitive and emotive issue. Much of this stems from the fact that there are not many areas of workable limestone in the country; those that are commercially attractive tend to be in regions of outstanding natural beauty, prized for conservation and recreation alike. The grounds for a clash of interests are only too clear. Conservationists in general are in opposition. The quarry companies stand accused of being interested only in profit. Locally there is widespread resentment against what is seen as environmental degradation in terms of pollution, the long term hydrological effects, the impact of heavy vehicles on country roads, a general despoiling of the countryside and the repercussions for the region's flora and fauna. Yet the industry brings with it direct and indirect employment to many who live in the region, thereby making a substantial (albeit short term) contribution to the local economy. More significantly, central government policy recognises that minerals are an important national resource and their exploitation makes an essential contribution to the nation's prosperity and quality of life.[1] In short, the debate may be perceived as a matter of national economics versus a local amenity.

The Mendip Hills in Somerset represent a unique and ecologically fragile environment. The region as a whole is relatively small and compact. Considerable local concern has been generated over plans to increase the size and capacity of limestone quarrying in Mendip, which many feel is not a large enough area to sustain any further mineral extraction without suffering escalating and irreversible damage to the character and environment of the whole region. The local debate, which has become increasingly highly charged and speculative, to a great extent also reflects the unease felt in other regions with similar problems. It was therefore judged that Mendip would provide a useful case study, as the basis for an investigation that might separate fact from fiction, both for the benefit of local people, and more widely. At the same time such an event would give local people the chance to express some of their own concerns and viewpoints on the subject.

As part of their respective autumn series of lectures and seminars, the Royal Bath and West of England Society and the Royal Geographical Society (Western Region) combined to hold a joint seminar on 23rd October 1993 with the object of discussing the implications of Limestone Quarrying in the United Kingdom, with special reference to the Mendip Hills.

It was wholly *apropos* that these two Societies should join forces to run a seminar directed at approaching the subject in a serious, objective and scholarly way. Both have strong interests in the region. The Royal Bath & West of England Society is an old and respected organisation, formed in 1777 with the object of encouraging agriculture, arts, manufacture and commerce throughout the region. In addition it conducts or financially assists practical and scientific investigation, as well as promoting technical education into agriculture, horticulture and forestry, including associated arts, manufacture and commerce. Throughout the year the Society also organises and holds a number of important shows and exhibitions connected with these activities. The Society's library and archives contain a wealth of important regional historical information in over two hundred years of agricultural records.

Ever since the Royal Geographical Society was founded in 1830, it has been a major source of geographical information and a focal point for British geographical and exploration activity. Despite a constantly changing world, the objectives of the Society have remained the same as those defined by Queen Victoria in the Society's Royal Charter, namely — 'the advancement of geographical science' and 'the improvement and diffusion of geographical knowledge'. These geographical studies are being seen as increasingly relevant to many of the most urgent global issues of today and the future, especially those relating to environmental degradation, expanding populations, nature conservation, resources and sustainability. The Society has recently established five regions outside London which run a full calendar of events throughout the year to supplement the London schedule of lectures and meetings. The Western Regional Committee is based on Bristol to serve the interests of the South West of England.

The declared aim of this seminar was to examine the geological, environmental and economic effects of limestone quarrying in a cool, objective and factual forum, using the Mendip Hills as a model. To achieve this, the meeting was structured around a programme of introductory lectures in the morning, in each of which an expert speaker developed a particular aspect of the subject. These lectures provided the introductory framework for an extensive discussion and open forum in which both the panel and audience, with widely differing views and experience of the subject, were able to raise and debate differing aspects. Two people made particularly useful contributions to the debate, and we have therefore invited them to contribute papers to these proceedings; they are Richard Moon, of the Environment Department of Somerset County Council, and Eunice Overend, whose knowledge of the history of the area, in the context of its flora and fauna, is well recognised.

The seminar was ably chaired by Sir John Quicke, a past president of the Royal Bath & West of England Society, who ensured in particular that the meeting provided neither a soap box for environmental objectors, nor a lobby platform for commercial interests. The proceedings of the seminar have been summarised and edited by Frank Raymond. To them both, to the speakers, and to all those who contributed to the debate, I should like to extend the warm appreciation and thanks of the Organising Committee.

The Organising Committee also particularly wishes to acknowledge and thank a number of people and organisations, without whose support and assistance it would not have been possible to run this event. First to National Westminster Bank plc, who have generously supported the production of this publication; to Burgess Salmon (Solicitors) of Bristol and to Somerset County Council for their valuable financial sponsorship; to Brigadier Simon Firth, Chief Executive of the Royal Bath & West of England Society, for kindly permitting the use of its facilities; to Miss Alison Glazebrook, Programme Coordinator at the Royal Geographical Society, London for her advice and help; and to Mr Christopher Cooper of Hampton Printing, Bristol for the loan of his personal helicopter in which a preliminary aerial reconnaissance of the Mendip area was made. In particular, as the Coordinating Chairman, I should like to give my personal thanks to my 'team' of willing helpers — Neil Ray of the Royal Geographical Society (Western Region), and Paul Hooper (Assistant Secretary), Mandy Adler, Valerie Legg and Susan Reid all from the Royal Bath & West of England Society.

Finally, the object of this publication is to present a record of the day's proceedings. In no way does it purport to represent a policy document, nor should it be taken to be any kind of official inquiry into the future of quarrying. It is produced in the form of a conference report, centred around contributions from the main speakers. All those who attended the seminar will receive a copy; it is also being made available through commercial bookshops in the hope that the subject will stimulate further interest and awareness from members of the general public. It should certainly have more than just a parochial appeal since, as has been pointed out elsewhere by Frank Raymond, the seminar was exceptional for having concentrated more on perceived shortcomings in national strategy than focusing (as might have been expected) on matters of purely local interest. In particular the Department of the Environment Mineral Planning Guidance Notes[2] came in for considerable criticism, both in relation to the apparent insensitivity of central government to local concerns, many of which centre on environmental and social issues, and to the failure of both government and industry to investigate alternative materials[3] in a sufficiently rigorous and imaginative manner.

Those hoping to find a definitive statement of either endorsement or condemnation are likely to be disappointed. It is not the purpose of the editor to express any opinion; only to record the discussions and tenor of the seminar. If any consensus does emerge, it probably represents a balance of opinion recognising economic realities and the inevitability of continued quarrying operations. Certainly the view was widely expressed that any increase from the present rate of mineral extraction was likely to be environmentally unsustainable; even at present levels, environmental damage was an inevitable price to pay for the region's contribution to Society's continuing demand for irreplaceable resources to meet economic growth and to maintain present living standards.[4] The problem now is to find some form of acceptable equilibrium.

John Hemsley
Chairman, Joint Organising Committee
The Wrangle, Compton Martin, Somerset.

1. *The Minerals Industry Performance Study*. Report prepared by Groundwork Associates Ltd. (for Department of Environment Minerals and Land Reclamation Division), HMSO, 1991, p.11.
2. Mineral Planning Guidance Notes [MPG] are published at intervals by the DoE to promulgate the official national requirement forecasts. MPG6 is the latest document which was available in draft form only at the time of the seminar. Nevertheless concern was expressed by many delegates over the validity of the data base used for forecasting and planning, as this was felt to have provided seriously flawed assumptions. It was therefore perhaps unfortunate that the DoE in London deemed it inappropriate to send a representative to answer factual questions relating to MPG6.
3. This applies particularly to the use of limestone for aggregate in the construction industry (road building), which was felt by a number of participants to represent the misuse of a scarce natural resource. Furthermore the present relative low cost of limestone provided little incentive to encourage research into alternative materials.
4. Although the subject received only passing reference at the seminar, some concern was expressed at the lack of evidence establishing a clear correlation between the construction of more roads and increased economic prosperity. This theme has been developed by Professor John Whitelegg, Department of Transport Studies at Lancaster University (see Tickell, O., 'Driven by Dogma', *Geographical* (RGS Magazine), October 1993, pp. 20 - 24).

MINERAL PLANNING GUIDANCE NOTES 6

Shortly before these proceedings were published the Government issued the latest version of MPG6. The new guidelines confirm that land-won sources of primary aggregates will remain the principal component of supply. However, an increasing proportion of the supply is planned to come from imports from outside England and Wales and from secondary and recycled materials.

The landbank requirement has been reduced from 10 years to 7 years from county areas for sand and gravel, although a longer (unspecified) period is indicated for hard rock.

For the South West region the guidelines envisage a total demand of 820M tonnes to 2006. This is made up of 610 Mt for regional needs and 210 Mt for exports to other regions. Some 715 Mt will be from primary land sources of which 610 Mt will be crushed rock. So far as other sources of supply for the region's needs are concerned it has been assumed that 60 Mt may be provided from secondary and recycled materials.

INTRODUCTION

On behalf of the Royal Bath and West of England Society and the Royal Geographical Society, may I commend to you these papers arising from a seminar, which was organised by a joint committee of the two Societies chaired by John Hemsley.

The subject they chose, Limestone Quarrying, is of national importance because of the key role that quarried limestone plays in the construction industry in this country. The Mendips, that small but scenically beautiful range of hills is one of the most important sources of that limestone. I had the opportunity to fly over those hills as part of my preparation to take the chair for the seminar, and I was quite unprepared for the scale of the quarrying activity that unfolded below me — activity, much of it in East Mendip, which although so far concealed from most of those who travel through the area must become increasingly visible and intrusive.

During my visit I learned that the area licensed for future quarrying is considerably more extensive than that already quarried, and that some experts believe that it should be possible to continue quarrying, at something like the present rate of output, without causing unacceptable environmental damage. Unfortunately the caveat, 'the present rate of output', is now in doubt; for the most recent forecast from the Department of the Environment envisages that, in order to meet the predicted future national demand for aggregates, the rate of limestone extraction from the Mendips will have to be doubled — from the present 15M tonnes per year to 32M tonnes.

Whatever one's view may be about the likely impact of the present rate of extraction, there must surely be legitimate concern about the huge increase in output that is now proposed, a concern shared equally by members of both Societies — hence the seminar. So that that debate should be as well-informed as possible a number of experts were asked to talk on different aspects of the Mendips of relevance to the overall subject of quarrying — the geology and water resources of the area; its ecology, natural features and tourist importance; and the role of the quarrying industry in local employment, and in providing a key basic material for the needs of modern society.

Thus I invited Ramous Gallois of the Geological Survey, in a paper written jointly with his colleague David Harrison, to describe the occurence of limestone deposits in the UK, and the particular features of the Mendip limestones; Peter Smart, of the Geography Department at Bristol University to describe the special hydrological features of the limestones; Willie Stanton to look at the ecology of the area and its tourist potential, and to speculate on some alternative sources of aggregates.

Turning to more immediate questions, David Tidmarsh, managing director of one of the main quarry operators, described how the national demand projections for aggregate supply are developed, and the contribution that Mendip limestone makes to that demand. The consequential requirement for Local Authorities to make land available to meet that future demand, and the problems, and conflicts, posed by this requirement, were examined in the final paper, by Humphrey Temperley, Chairman of the Environment Committee of Somerset County Council. The ensuing debate was stimulating.

John Quicke
Newton St. Cyres,
Exeter, Devonshire.

LIMESTONE AS A RESOURCE AND ITS ALTERNATIVES

David Harrison and Ramous Gallois
British Geological Survey

INTRODUCTION

Limestones are ancient sedimentary rocks composed of calcium carbonate or calcium/magnesium carbonate that formed by chemical precipitation either directly from freshwater lakes or the sea or, much more commonly, to form the hard parts of a wide variety of animals and plants including shells, corals and algae. The great majority of limestones can therefore be classified as predominantly inorganic (precipitated) or organic (accumulation of biogenic remains) in origin (Table 1). The most common type of inorganic limestone (oolitic limestone) was formed in turbulent, shallow seas in subtropical climates (similar to those of the Bahamas Banks at the present time) in which particles of sand or shell rolled about on the sea floor and became progressively coated with lime to form pellets,

pisoids or ooids (from the Greek pisos, a pea and oon, an egg). Some of the best British examples of oolitic limestones are those in the Carboniferous limestone of the Mendip Hills and the Jurassic limestones of the Cotswold Hills (Figure 1).

Many limestones still contain enough of their original structure to enable them to be recognised as having formed as coral reefs, shell banks or as carbonate oozes composed of the hard parts of billions of microscopic plants or animals.

Almost all the limestones preserved in Britain were deposited in marine environments. The plants and animals that generated calcareous hard parts relied on photosynthesis and mostly lived in clear, nutrient- and oxygen-rich, sunlit waters at relatively shallow depths (less than 100 m). Their hard parts were subjected to wave action and strong currents with the result that many limestones are composed of finely broken debris, and calcareous mud produced by the activities of boring algae and bacteria on the larger shell particles. Not surprisingly, most limestones are composite in origin; they contain recognisable shells and other organic debris, together with calcareous mud that may be of organic or inorganic origin. Because of the relatively high solubility of calcium carbonate and the porous nature of most limestones, almost all limestones contain large amounts of calcium carbonate that has been precipitated as secondary crystalline material (called spar cement), in many cases long after the original formation of the deposit. Dolomites (mixed magnesium/ calcium carbonates) have mostly formed from the secondary alteration of normal limestones under the action of magnesium-rich groundwater.

The surface rocks of about 15% of England and Wales are limestones, and they occupy extensive areas at depth beneath younger rocks. They range in age from 550 million (Cambrian) to 60 million years old (Cretaceous), but they

---

TABLE 1
ORIGIN OF LIMESTONES

Organic	Coral reefs Algal reefs Shell banks Pelagic oozes
Clastic (mostly organic)	Shell, crinoid and coral debris, calcareous mud
Inorganic (precipitated)	Ooids, pisoids and pellets Stalactites and stalagmites Calcite cement
Composite	Most limestones

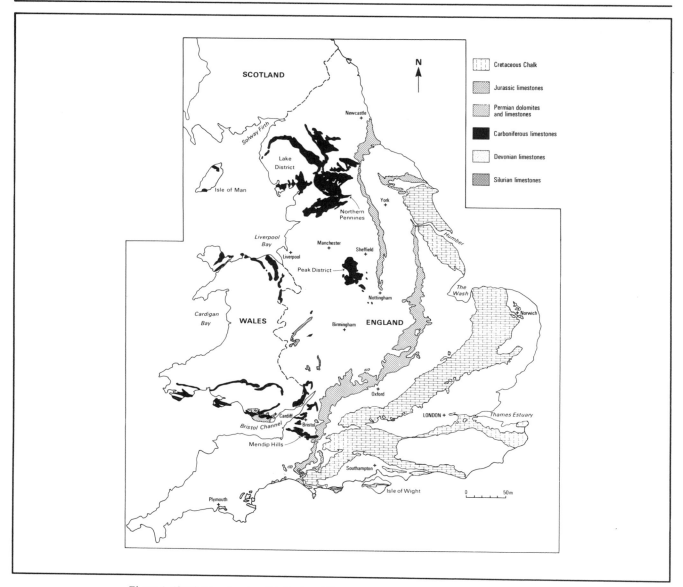

Figure 1 Sketch Map showing distribution of limestone, dolomite and chalk in England and Wales.

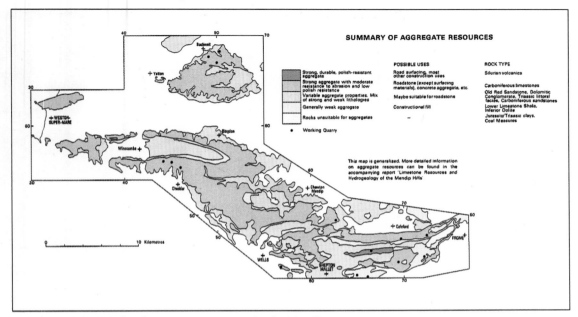

Plate 1: *Summary of aggregate resources in the Mendip area.* (Courtesy of The British Geological Survey).

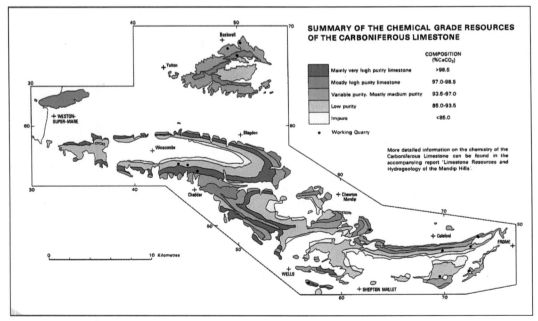

Plate 2: *Carboniferous limestone chemical grade resources in Mendip.* (Courtesy of The British Geological Survey).

Plate 3: *Stalagmites, stalactites and curtains adorn a fossil cave passage in Withymill Cave, Fairy Cave Quarry, East Mendip.* (Courtesy of Peter Smart).

Plate 4: *Whatley Quarry, eastern Mendip, one of the new generation of very large superquarries supplying crushed stone to South East England by rail.* (Courtesy of Peter Smart).

fall largely into four groups; the Carboniferous limestone (including the Mendip Hills), the Permian dolomites of northern England, the Jurassic limestones (including the Cotswold Hills), and the Cretaceous chalk.

USES OF LIMESTONES

Great Britain is fortunate in being well endowed with limestone resources, many of which are hard enough to be used as crushed rock aggregates, of sufficient purity to be used as a feedstock in the chemical, steel and glass industries, or of the required aesthetic appeal to be used as building stones.

Limestones are an important economic resource because of their physical properties and/or chemical composition (Table 2) which are directly related to many of their uses. They are also indirectly important because of their commonly fractured or porous nature and their ability to act as a host for fluids. The chalk is the most important single source of groundwater in the United Kingdom, and limestones beneath the North Sea act as the reservoir rocks for some of the larger oil and gas fields.

Some of the physical and chemical properties of limestones make them uniquely valuable for the purposes for which they are used - the beauty of Bath Stone which derives from its colour and texture, and the usefulness of the purer limestones as chemical feedstocks. Many uses, however, simply require large volumes of rock of a suitable

TABLE 2 WHY LIMESTONES ARE ECONOMICALLY IMPORTANT	
Physical properties	Hardness Softness Colour Texture Massive Bedded Fractured Permeability
Chemical composition	Impure calcium carbonate Pure calcium carbonate Dolomite

porosity and strength, irrespective of its chemical composition.

Limestone has a wide variety of applications (Figure 2), but its primary use is in the construction industry (Table 3) where it is the principal source of crushed rock aggregate in Britain, an essential raw material for cement manufacture, and also a source of building and ornamental stone.

Limestone is also important in steel and glass making, sugar refining, numerous chemical processes, as a mineral filler in paint, plastics and rubber and in agricultural

TABLE 3 GREAT BRITAIN PRODUCTION OF LIMESTONE BY END USE IN 1991 (UK MINERALS YEARBOOK 1992)					
CONSTRUCTIONAL USES - TOTAL 100.0 MILLION TONNES					
Building Stone 1.4	Roadstone 52.9	Railway Ballast 0.3	Concrete Aggregate 11.7	Cement 8.9	Others 24.8
NON-CONSTRUCTIONAL USES - TOTAL 7.7 MILLION TONNES					
Iron/steel 2.2	Glass making 0.2	Fillers 1.3	Agriculture 1.2	Others 2.8	

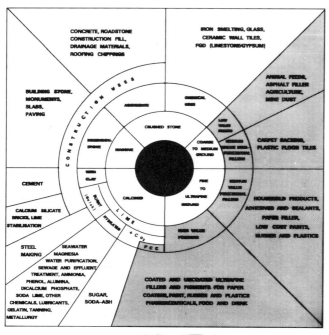

Figure 2 Major uses of limestone.

applications and water treatment. In these non-constructional or 'high-purity' applications, limestone (or lime derived from the burning of limestone) may be used either as a chemically reactive raw material or as an inert filler or pigment. Limestone used for construction, cement and in agriculture as a soil conditioner does not require high chemical purity. Limestone used for 'high purity' purposes accounts for a small and decreasing proportion of total limestone output.

CONSTRUCTIONAL USES

ROADSTONE

Roadstone is the largest single end use of limestone in the UK and many other countries. Modern roads are designed to be flexible, and to achieve this are made of discrete layers. The lowest layer, the 'sub-base', which typically consists of angular particles of rock up to 10 cm across, distributes the load onto the underlying subsoil. Above this the 'roadbase' acts as the main load-bearing layer: the sub-base and roadbase layers also drain the road. The surfacing layers are made up of a 'basecourse' and a thin 'top-course' or 'wearing-course'. Crushed limestone aggregates are most commonly used in the sub-base and roadbase layers where the stone is required to be strong, clean (free from clay) and with low porosity so that it does not retain water. Limestones are typically less suitable than many sandstones or igneous rocks for use in road surfacing materials, which are required to be hard wearing and skid resistant. Many limestones are relatively soft and become abraded by traffic wear, and almost all become relatively easily polished and give rise to slippery surfaces. Some specifications for roadstone aggregates are given in Table 4.

CONCRETE AGGREGATES

Concrete is usually made from a mixture of cement, coarse aggregate (gravel, crushed limestone or other hard rock) and fine aggregate (generally sand). The properties of the aggregate affect many of the characteristics of the concrete, including its density, strength, durability, thermal conductivity, and its susceptibility to shrinkage and creep. The shape and surface texture of the aggregate particles and the distribution of the particle sizes are important factors that influence the workability and strength of the concrete. In addition aggregates used in concrete must not have an adverse effect on the setting properties of the cement or on the long-term stability of the concrete. Suitable aggregates must be hard, durable and clean and they must be free of clay, organic material, pyrite (iron sulphide) and disordered forms of silica which may be subject to attack by alkalis (ASR reaction) that cause expansion and cracking in concrete (the so-called concrete cancer).

BUILDING STONE

Limestones have been popular building or ornamental stones since the earliest times, as evidenced by the Egyptian

TABLE 4
TYPICAL SPECIFICATION REQUIREMENTS FOR ROADSTONE AGGREGATES

Particle density (specific gravity)	generally > 2.65
Water absorption (an indicator of porosity)	<2%
Flakiness index (shape factor)	<25 (for wearing-course) <35 (for general purposes)
Aggregate crushing value (ACV strength test)	generally <24 or <30
Aggregate impact value (AIV strength test) 10% fines value (strength test)	generally <25 >160 KN
Aggregate abrasion value (AAV surface wear test)	<14 for lightly trafficked sites or <10 for potentially dangerous sites
Los Angeles abrasion value (LAAV attrition test)	<40 (for wearing-course) <50 (for basecourse)
Sulphate soundness test (disintegration by weathering test)	<18% magnesium sulphate loss

Note: This Table shows specifications relating to typical British and American standards. Where test value limits are not specified, then guideline values are shown.

pyramids and Greek statues. Although formerly very important, the use of natural stone in building in the UK is now a relatively small specialist market. Aesthetic appeal (colour, texture etc.) is a primary consideration in the choice of limestone, but its potential durability is also important and affects the way in which it can be used. The durability of limestones in the British climate is largely a function of their pore size. Limestones with low porosity (e.g. Carboniferous limestone), or with large pores from which water can easily drain (e.g. Cotswold stone) are usually suitable as external building stones because they have a low susceptibility to frost damage. Muddy limestones such as Purbeck marble are only suitable for indoor use.

OTHER AGGREGATE USES

Substantial quantities of limestone aggregate are used as constructional fill in land reclamation, site levelling and embankment construction. The specifications for such materials are generally undemanding and many of the softer or more porous limestones may be used. Limestone aggregates are also used for drainage materials beneath large underground pipes and in filter drains. In the past, limestone aggregates were commonly used for railway ballast, but their relatively low resistance to abrasion meant that they had to be more frequently replaced than igneous rock, which is now usually preferred for this purpose.

CEMENT

Cement is made by heating (calcining) a mixture of about 75% limestone and 25% clay to form a calcium silicate clinker which is then ground and mixed with a small amount of gypsum which retards and controls the setting properties. Impurities in the raw materials which may affect the quality of the cement include magnesium, fluorine, phosphorus, lead, zinc, alkalis and sulphides. For example, the specification for ordinary Portland cement requires that the cement should not contain more than 6% magnesium oxide (MgO). This means that any limestone with more than 3% of magnesium carbonate ($MgCO_3$) is unsuitable, and excludes all dolomitic limestones. However, there are few other stringent specifications for limestone in cement manufacture and relatively impure deposits can be utilised providing the limestone contains at least 80% calcium carbonate.

TABLE 5
ESTIMATES OF CONSUMPTION OF INDUSTRIAL (NON-CONSTRUCTIONAL) LIMESTONE IN 1989 (MODIFIED FROM ROGER TYM AND PARTNERS, 1990)

Use	Consumption (thousand tonnes)
Iron and Steel	2872
Soda Ash (sodium carbonate)	990
Sugar Refining	245
Glass Making	325
Precipitated Calcium Carbonate	100
Other Chemical Uses	173
Animal Feeds	300
Agriculture	1950
Sea Water Magnesia	142
Paper Filler and Coating	305
Rubber and Plastics	155
Other Pigments	340
Total	7897

NON-CONSTRUCTIONAL USES: CHEMICAL

Limestone is used in a number of industries (Table 5) where its chemical properties as a basic oxide, a neutralising agent, a source of calcium, and/or a flux are important. Some examples are outlined below. Iron production, glass making and flue-gas desulphurisation use raw limestone, but most of the remaining processes use limestones that have been burnt to produce lime.

IRON AND STEEL INDUSTRY

Limestone or lime is used as a flux because it promotes fusion of the slag (mostly silica compounds produced by the breakdown of the iron ore), and assists in the removal of unwanted impurities such as silica and phosphorus. High-purity limestones with low sulphur, silica and phosphorus contents are generally specified for this process but, in common with many limestone end uses, chemical consistency and a local supply are usually the main criteria for choosing any particular source.

GLASS MAKING

Most glass is made by melting silica sand and soda ash (sodium carbonate) with limestone. The limestone imparts durability to lime-soda-silica glasses. Very high purity limestones (>98.5% $CaCO_3$ or 55.2% CaO with very low contents of iron and other elements) are generally required for this application because even very small amounts of impurities either colour or weaken the glass. The amounts of limestone used in glassmaking are not large and consistency is generally more important than absolute chemical values.

SUGAR REFINING

Limestone and lime are used in the preparation of sugar from sugar beet, as part of the purification process to adjust pH, and assist in precipitation of impurities. High-grade limestones with at least 96% $CaCO_3$ and low silica and iron contents (<1% SiO_2, <0.3% Fe_2O_3) are usually specified.

FLUE-GAS DESULPHURISATION (FGD)

Concern over acid rain has led to the increasing use of limestone to reduce emissions of sulphur dioxide from coal- and oil-fired power stations. The limestone-gypsum process involves passing the flue gases through a circulating slurry of limestone and water. The sulphur dioxide dissolves and reacts with the limestone to form calcium sulphite which is then oxidised to calcium sulphate (gypsum). Limestone with a minimum $CaCO_3$ content of 95% and with limitations on certain impurities is normally specified. Experimental power plants using fluidised-bed combustion, in which a mixture of powdered coal and limestone is burned thereby trapping the sulphur at source, have yet to result in large-scale commercial operations.

WATER PURIFICATION AND EFFLUENT TREATMENT

Hydrated lime is used in the treatment of drinking water to adjust the acidity (pH) and to remove impurities. Lime is also used to lessen some of the harmful chemical and bacterial components of sewage sludge and to neutralise acidic industrial effluents.

NON-CONSTRUCTIONAL USES: FILLERS AND PIGMENTS

Limestone is relatively easily ground to a fine powder which is non-toxic, chemically inert and generally white in colour. These properties ensure that limestone powders are extensively used as fillers in a diverse range of products where the primary purpose of the filler is to add bulk to the product cheaply. These include adhesives, cheap paints and carpet backing. Some fillers make use of the chemical properties of the limestone, for example as a source of calcium in animal feeds and as an acidity regulator in some pharmaceutical and agricultural products.

Many high-volume uses of limestone powders, including carpet backing, asphalt manufacture and as coal-mine dust, do not require pure limestone. In contrast, powders used in pharmaceuticals and food are required to be of very high purity and are generally made by digesting limestone in acid and then precipitating pure calcium carbonate from solution. Limestone powders used as fillers in paper, plastics and the more expensive paints typically require particle-sizes within a closely defined range and high brightness (whiteness) values. They must also mix evenly with the other constituents.

LIMESTONE RESOURCES IN ENGLAND AND WALES

Limestones are common rocks and occur extensively in all the continents of the earth; they range in age from over 3000 million years (Precambrian) to a few thousand years (Recent). Deposits of limestone are widespread in England and Wales (Figure 1). The lithological characters of the limestones are in many cases variable and they may contain impurities such as clay, sand and flint which may make them unsuitable for many economic uses. In some cases they have been affected by geological processes, such as mineralisation, dolomitisation or by faulting and folding of the strata, which make then chemically unsuitable or difficult to work. Nevertheless, large areas of England and Wales are underlaid by thick, relatively uniform deposits of limestone which form potential raw materials for many

TABLE 6
ESTIMATED PRODUCTION OF LIMESTONE, INCLUDING DOLOMITE AND CHALK, BY AGE (GEOLOGICAL SYSTEM) IN GREAT BRITAIN (1990)

Geological system	% Total production for all end-uses
Cretaceous	10.2
Jurassic	7.8
Permian	11.5
Carboniferous	66.5
Devonian	1.5
Silurian	1.3
Cambrian/Precambrian	1.2
Total	132 million tonnes (of which around 8 million tonnes are used in high purity end uses)

industrial uses. The Carboniferous limestone is the major source of limestone raw materials in the UK (Table 6) due to its large outcrop, its consistent quality for a range of end uses, and the convenient location of many of the outcrops. Carboniferous limestones also typically form thick and consistent deposits which are relatively easy and cheap to work. In short, they are the preferred raw material for construction and industrial ('high purity') use and cement manufacture. Unfortunately, the Carboniferous limestone is also associated with high quality landscapes.

Large quantities of Permian magnesian limestone, Cretaceous chalk and Jurassic limestone are also worked, as are smaller amounts of Silurian and Devonian limestones (Table 6). These limestones do not offer the same range of desirable properties as Carboniferous limestones.

CARBONIFEROUS LIMESTONES

Carboniferous limestones are extensively quarried in the Mendips, South and North Wales, the Peak District, parts of the northern Pennines and around the fringes of the Lake District (Harrison, 1991). Most of the stone is used in the construction industry, but the outstanding chemical purity of the limestone in certain areas has resulted in the extraction of large amounts of limestone for high-purity (industrial) end uses.

The Peak District of Derbyshire supplies much of the high purity limestone consumed in the UK as well as large tonnages of aggregate. In contrast, the limestones of Wales and the Mendip Hills supply large amounts of crushed-rock aggregate and only small amounts of high purity stone. The differences in limestone production result directly from geological diversity in the limestone resources.

PEAK DISTRICT

The Carboniferous limestones of the Peak District are characteristically flat lying (low angles of dip) and are noted for their uniformity over wide areas (Harrison and Adlam, 1985). The Bee Low limestones (Table 7) are the most extensively quarried unit: they are consistently of very high purity (>98.5% $CaCO_3$) and of uniform chemistry

TABLE 7 CARBONIFEROUS LIMESTONE SUCCESSION IN THE PEAK DISTRICT	
Longstone Mudstones	up to 40 m
Eyam Limestones	10 - 40 m
Monsal Dale Limestones	50 - 375 m
Bee Low Limestones	70 - 213 m
Woo Dale Limestones	> 100 m

throughout the region. The underlying Woo Dale limestones are only marginally less pure, and together the two units total over 250 m of high purity limestone resources. The limestone sequence above the Bee Low limestones is more lithologically and chemically varied and less pure. Quarries in the Monsal Dale and Eyam limestones produce aggregates and cement whereas quarries producing high purity industrial limestones (as well as construction materials) are sited either in the Bee Low limestones or, to a lesser extent, in the Woo Dale limestones. Around 18 million tonnes of limestone are quarried each year from 25 quarries and one underground limestone mine. About 55% of total production is used for constructional purposes.

MENDIP HILLS

The Carboniferous limestone is the major rock type forming the Mendip Hills and is a large and important mineral resource. Large scale quarrying is principally for aggregates and all five formations present (Figure 3 and Plate 1) are capable of producing good quality roadstone (sub-base and roadbase) and concreting aggregates. Up to 20 million tonnes of limestone are quarried each year from 14 quarries, most of which are in the eastern Mendips. Limestones produced from the Mendip quarries usually

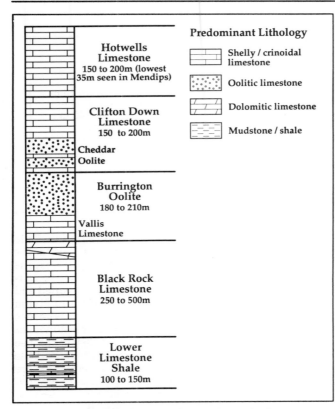

	Predominant Lithology	
Hotwells Limestone 150 to 200m (lowest 35m seen in Mendips)		Shelly / crinoidal limestone
Clifton Down Limestone 150 to 200m		Oolitic limestone
Cheddar Oolite		Dolomitic limestone
Burrington Oolite 180 to 210m		Mudstone / shale
Vallis Limestone		
Black Rock Limestone 250 to 500m		
Lower Limestone Shale 100 to 150m		

Figure 3 Carboniferous limestone succession in the Mendips (after Green and Welch, 1965).

contain more than 1% silica, magnesia and iron and are not generally suitable for non-constructional purposes. However, the thick middle part of the succession, the Burrington Oolite and equivalent beds, is of consistently high purity and is locally quarried for industrial grade limestone (Plate 2). The Mendip limestones, in contrast to those in the Peak District, are typically steeply dipping and highly faulted and it is this feature which is the significant constraint on developing industrial grade resources. The many fault zones, joints and cavities within the limestones are partially filled with brownish or yellowish clays and silts which are a potential contaminant of the limestone resources.

CRETACEOUS LIMESTONES: THE CHALK

The thick and extensive deposits of the chalk of eastern and southern England are an important source of limestone raw material which is used in the manufacture of cement, in agriculture and for chalk whiting, and as a fine chalk powder valued for its brightness in filler applications such as papermaking. Approximately 13 million tonnes of chalk are quarried annually.

Chalk is typically white, very fine grained and of a homogenous nature. Its deposition from microscopic algae has resulted in its generally high purity and lateral consistency over large areas. The chief impurities are flint and clay. The chalks of northern England are typically harder and contain less absorbed water (they are used as low-grade aggregates) than those of southern England (which are not used as aggregates).

PERMIAN DOLOMITES

Dolomites (carbonate rocks composed mainly of calcium magnesium carbonate) and dolomitic limestones of Permian age (the Magnesian limestone) occupy a narrow outcrop of easterly-dipping strata which extends from Newcastle to Nottingham. The Magnesian limestone is the prime source of dolomite in Britain but it varies markedly in its chemical and physical properties (Rendel, Palmer and Tritton, 1988) and extraction is mainly for aggregates (mostly fill or sub-base roadstone). Parts of the sequence, for example around Doncaster, contain rocks of higher chemical grade and several quarries produce a high grade industrial stone for use in seawater magnesia, glass manufacture, refractories and as a flux in blast furnaces. Annual production of Permian dolomites and limestones totals around 12 million tonnes.

JURASSIC LIMESTONES

Jurassic limestones outcrop widely from North Yorkshire to Dorset. They are mostly porous and relatively soft, and are used in cement manufacture and as building stone. They are also locally worked for aggregates (mainly for fill or sub-base roadstone materials) in areas where better quality aggregates are difficult to obtain. These limestones are only locally of high purity and are usually thin and may be laterally impersistent. Total production in 1990 was about 8 million tonnes, from about 60 quarries most of which were small-scale workings. Some larger developments are associated with cement works.

SILURIAN AND DEVONIAN LIMESTONES

Small, locally important resources of Silurian and Devonian limestone are present in the Welsh Borders and in Devon. In the Welsh Borders, the Silurian strata contain three limestone formations, comprising muddy limestones and calcareous siltstones which are locally suitable for constructional fill and roadstone aggregates. In south Devon, around Plymouth and Torquay, hard Devonian limestones are quarried for a range of aggregate materials and for the production of cement. The more massive limestones contain some high purity stone.

LIMESTONE PRODUCTION IN GREAT BRITAIN

Production of limestone in Great Britain has increased dramatically since the 1960s (Figure 4) and production figures illustrate the importance of limestone as a natural resource, particularly of aggregate materials. In 1991, production of limestone (including dolomite and chalk) totalled 108 million tonnes, of which only about 8 million tonnes were used for high purity industrial uses. Thus over 92% of total limestone production in Great Britain was used as roadstone, concrete aggregate or for other constructional purposes (Table 3).

Road construction is by far the largest consumer of limestone in Great Britain, most (about 40 million tonnes per annum) being used in uncoated form. This is not surprising as the properties of limestone are ideally suitable for roadstone, and one mile of motorway construction typically requires about 200,000 tonnes of aggregate. Large amounts of crushed limestone are also used as concrete

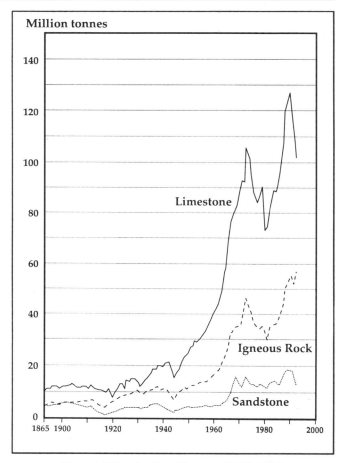

Figure 4 UK production of limestone (1865 - 1991).

aggregate, and the production of cement is also a major consumer of limestone raw materials. Nearly 1.5 million tonnes of limestone (mainly Jurassic limestones) were quarried for building stone in 1991. In the non-constructional (or high purity) market sector, most limestone is used in iron and steel production (Table 3). The iron/steel and glass industries represent high volume

TABLE 8
ESTIMATED LIMESTONE PRICES, EX QUARRY, IN 1989
(ADAPTED FROM ROGER TYM AND PARTNERS, 1990).

Use and Processing	Price (£/tonne)
Aggregates (crushed limestone)	2.0 - 4.5
Glass (medium ground limestone)	7.5 - 8.0
Paper (filler grade)	10.0 - 30.0
Various (lime)	30.0 - 45.0
Paper (coating grade)	40.0 - 100.0
Pharmaceuticals (precipitated calcium carbonate)	250.0 - 380.0

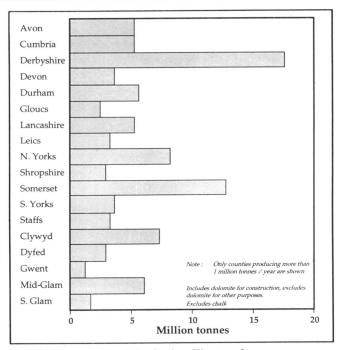

Note: Only counties producing more than 1 million tonnes / year are shown

Includes dolomite for construction, excludes dolomite for other purposes. Excludes chalk

Figure 5 Production of limestone by county in England and Wales in 1991.

uses of low price limestone, as do construction materials, agricultural limestone, asphalt filler and mine dust. In contrast, uses such as fillers and pigments have a higher commercial value, although in volume terms such uses are minor (Table 8).

The price of a limestone product is largely governed by the cost of extraction, processing and transportation. The high capital costs of quarrying, due to the high investment in machinery to work and process the stone, has led to the development of superquarries that can produce large outputs over long periods of time. Thus, in the Peak District, the rationalisation and mechanisation that has taken place in the quarrying industry since the Second World War has resulted in a decline in the total number of active quarries from over 50 in 1939 to 25 today. Similarly, in the Mendips the investment in larger quarries has reduced the number of aggregate quarries from 21 in 1973 to 14 now. However in both areas there has been a marked increase in total annual production. Some of these quarries, such as Whatley Quarry (ARC) and Torr Works (Foster Yeoman) in the Mendips, have the capacity to produce about 7 million tonnes of limestone aggregate per year. Both have direct access to the railway network, and around 75% of their output is transported to London and the South East by rail. The production of limestone by county in 1991 in England and Wales was dominated by the large productions in South Wales, Derbyshire and Somerset /Avon (Figure 5).

The South East region has no indigenous sources of hard rock. However sand and gravel, which in recent years have been worked in similar quantities to limestones in the UK (Figure 6), occur extensively in the region and when taken into account the region is a major producer of aggregates. The South East region is the major British market for aggregates; it consumes about 30% of the total production in England with the result that, despite its local production, it is a major importer of crushed rock (Figure 7). In 1989, the South East region used 74 million tonnes of

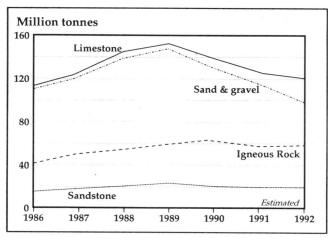

Figure 6 UK Bulk minerals production (1986 - 1992).

aggregates but only produced from sand and gravel pits within the region about 37 million tonnes. The remainder came from crushed rock sources (21 million tonnes, mainly from the Mendips and Leicestershire), marine-dredged sand and gravel (15 million tonnes) and a small amount from secondary/recycled aggregates.

The inter-regional flows of crushed rock are dominated by the flow of materials from regions of surplus such as the South West, East Midlands, and North Wales, to the major deficit regions of the South East, West Midlands and North West (Figure 7). Most of this crushed rock is limestone, although large amounts of igneous rocks are quarried in Leicestershire.

ALTERNATIVE RESOURCES

Limestones as raw materials are rarely without substitute. However, because of their many attributes (hardness, calcium carbonate content, brightness, etc.) there is no single mineral alternative and substitution is not always simple or inexpensive.

In the industrial (high purity) limestone sector limestone, chalk and dolomite are fundamental feedstocks for many industries which utilise the chemical properties of the stone, and there are few substitutes for them. However, limestone (chalk) used as a filler in paper and paint can be substituted by kaolin or talc, although these materials are much more expensive. Indeed, one of the advantages of limestone as a raw material is that it is relatively inexpensive and there has been a long-term trend in some industries which did not formerly use limestone to favour the use of limestone over other raw materials. In other words, the current trend is substitution into limestone.

In the construction industry crushed limestone aggregates are widely used primarily because they are relatively cheap and fulfil the range of technical specifications. Hard limestone aggregate can be replaced by other crushed stone such as quartzite, sandstone, granite, dolerite and basalt, but these are commonly more expensive to work and, as a consequence, the products are more expensive. Even in the Mendips area there are other potential aggregate resources (Plate 1). Large amounts of rock other than limestone are quarried in England and Wales, but resources of these rocks are not as large or as widespread as those of limestone and many of them are less conveniently situated with respect to their markets. Large deposits of these rocks occur in coastal locations in Scotland, Ireland and Scandinavia and various sites are under consideration for development as 'coastal superquarries' that would supply crushed rock aggregates directly by sea-going bulk carriers. The Glensanda Quarry at Loch Linnhe in Scotland (Foster Yeoman) is the only operational coastal superquarry in the UK; it currently produces 5 million tonnes of crushed granite aggregates per annum. Other planned schemes include proposals to extract the igneous rock anorthosite from South Harris (Redland Aggregates), to quarry anorthosite from south-west Norway (Tarmac) and to extract sandstone from Bantry Bay in Ireland (Wimpey). The successful development of these schemes will depend on a number of factors including environmental impact, local and EEC planning controls, the capital costs of production and crushing, the provision of suitable docking and loading facilities at both quarry and destination, customer acceptance of the quarried products, and the ability to displace existing products from a market which is currently static or declining. Thus the recent government proposal to increase the motorway network, if implemented, could

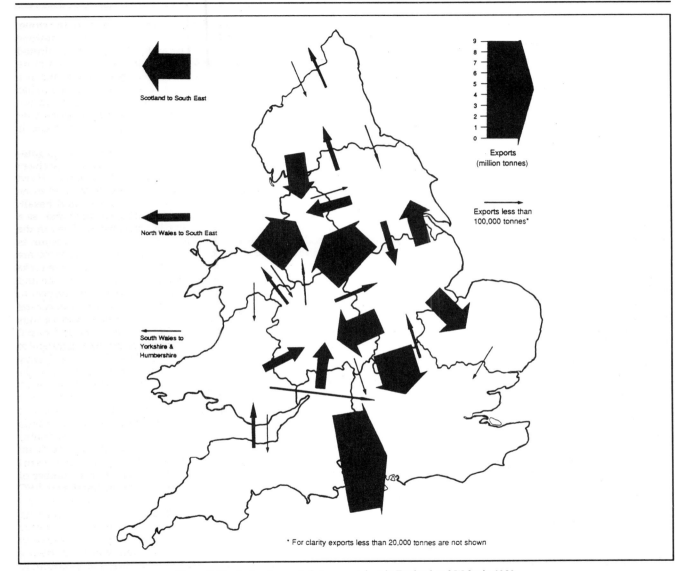

Figure 7 Crushed rock exports betweeen regions in England and Wales in 1989.

increase the need for aggregates from coastal superquarries.

There is continuing interest in the substitution of quarried aggregates by alternative materials such as china clay waste, slate waste, colliery spoil, construction wastes, slag, and power station ash (Whitbread and others, 1991). Such materials are termed secondary aggregates. Some are currently used in the construction industry, but the geographical location of many of these wastes is such that they require high transport costs to get them to their point of use. For the most part, as the name 'wastes' implies, they are also poor quality materials that have previously had no economic value. For example the china clay waste deposits of Cornwall and Devon are vast (over 600 million tonnes), but the material is a poorly sorted mixture of quartz sand, soft partially kaolinised granite and clay. Even when sorted and washed they are only suitable as the fine part of a concrete mix or as constructional fill and cannot substitute for coarse aggregate such as crushed limestone. There are an estimated 2,000 million tonnes of colliery spoil in tips, mainly in Yorkshire, Nottinghamshire and South Wales. Colliery waste, however, is composed of a mixture of mudstone and sandstone and is only really suitable for low grade aggregate uses (constructional fill): it would not meet the specifications for roadstone aggregates. Around 13 million tonnes of pulverised fuel ash (flyash) is produced annually from British power stations. Some is used for concrete block making and constructional fill, but its potential to reduce the national demand for aggregates is necessarily limited. In Wales there are over 400 million tonnes of slate waste in tips. A small amount has been used in the lower layers of road constructions, but most of the tips are in rural areas far distant from major road schemes. Blast furnace and steel slags have also been used locally for roadstone, but the volumes of these wastes are relatively small.

Around 24 million tonnes of demolition and construction wastes are produced each year in Britain. Of these, over 11 million tonnes are re-used, mainly as fill. They represent the largest use of secondary aggregates in the UK, largely because they are generated at or close to their point of use. In addition, over 80% of ashphalted road planings are re-used, mainly as fill or as roadbase material.

Although secondary aggregates are utilised in Britain and are a substitute for some rock aggregates, their mixed quality and the high cost of transporting them from remote locations mean that secondary aggregates do not significantly reduce the demand for crushed rock and sand and gravel in England and Wales.

ECONOMIC AND ENVIRONMENTAL CONSIDERATIONS

The economic and environmental considerations that need to be taken into account when deciding whether or not any particular limestone or other rock should be quarried, either as a new working or as a continuation of existing workings, include issues of local, regional and national importance. Some of these issues are examined in the papers presented at this seminar. Issues, in particular those that involve a conflict of interest between local desires and regional or national needs, are dealt with in government policy statements. For example, the intention to improve the trunk-road network and to expand the motorway network to make Britain more competitive in Europe will automatically lead to a greater demand for roadstone. The Mineral Planning Guidelines (MPG6, Department of the Environment, 1993) set out the key planning factors which have to be taken into consideration when the sources of this additional roadstone are chosen.

An important prerequisite of all such planning is the availability of accurate data on which the best decisions can be made. In the case of quarrying for limestone or other hard rock, it is important not only to know precisely where the local deposits are, both at surface and at depth, but also to know the location and properties of other rocks throughout Britain so that all possible alternative sources can be considered. These data are provided by the maps of the British Geological Survey, mostly at the large scale of 1 to 10,560 (six inches to one mile) or its metric equivalent of 1 to 10, 000. The whole of the Mendips region is covered by modern geological maps at this scale, and on these maps rock outcrops as small as 10 x 10 m are accurately depicted.

Once possible sources of rock have been identified and shown as having the properties necessary to satisfy the particular user, cost becomes a major factor in the decision making process. The cost to the customer at the point of

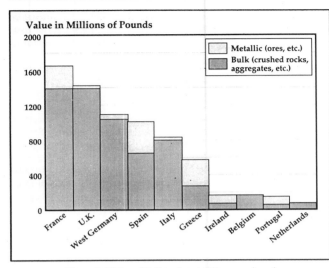

Value in Millions of Pounds

Metallic (ores, etc.)
Bulk (crushed rocks, aggregates, etc.)

Figure 8 Value of bulk and metalliferous minerals produced in the EEC by country in 1991.

use is almost wholly governed by the cost of winning and processing stone and the cost of transportation. There are, however, important financial implications at both local and national level that also need to be considered. Quarries, by their very nature, are mostly in rural areas where they, and the jobs and locally-spent money that they generate, represent an important part of the local economy. The equipment and consumables that they use, assuming that they are made in the UK, also contribute to employment outside the local area. There is also a strong financial incentive for the UK to make use of its natural resources. Britain has abundant reserves of industrial limestones and other rocks that are suitable for aggregate and similar uses, but is deficient in rocks containing metalliferous minerals (Figure 8). We import large amounts of aluminium and iron as ores, and these and other metals as finished products. Because of their bulk and the cost of transportation there is little scope for Britain to export its industrial minerals to offset the balance of payments, although some china clay and other specialist clays are exported as well as marine sand and gravel. Proposals to import aggregates from Ireland or Norway would further increase the current trade imbalance.

The environmental costs of proceeding with any particular quarry, which are examined in Willie Stanton's paper, are much more difficult to quantify. In addition to measurable factors such as possible water pollution and noise and dust hazard, and factors that can be qualitatively assessed such as the loss of or possible damage to habitats of local, national or world-wide importance, there are also such intangibles as the aesthetic appeal of scenery and the solitude of places untouched by man and little changed since the retreat of the Pleistocene ice sheets tens of thousands of years ago.

CONCLUSIONS

Britain is rich in limestone resources that have important uses in many industries. Some of these uses rely on the particular physical property (e.g. building stone, whiting for paper making) or chemical properties (e.g. cement manufacture, iron and steel making) of the limestones and there are few other materials that can perform the same functions. Certainly none of them can do so as cheaply as limestone. The great bulk of the limestone worked in Britain is used as aggregate in roadstone, concrete and fill, for which there are both natural and man-made alternatives. These include other rocks in situ and in waste tips, and wastes from the iron making and power generation industries. However, limestones continue to be the most plentiful, and in many cases the most easily worked resource, and few of the alternatives can compete on cost at the present time.

ACKNOWLEDGEMENTS

The authors would like to thank their colleague, Mr D. E. Highley, for commenting on the text.

This paper is published by permission of the Director, British Geological Survey (NERC).

REFERENCES

British Geological Survey 1965. One Inch Series (1 to 63,360 scale) Geological Sheet 281 (Frome). Southampton: Ordnance Survey.

British Geological Survey 1984. 1 to 50,000 Series Geological Sheet 280 (Wells). Southampton: Ordnance Survey.

British Geological Survey 1993. *United Kingdom Minerals Yearbook 1992*. (Keyworth, Nottingham: British Geological Survey).

Department of the Environment 1991. *National Collation of the 1989 Aggregate Minerals Survey*. DoE.

Green, G. W. 1992. *Bristol and Gloucester region. British Regional Geology*. London: HMSO.

Green, G. W. and Welch, F. B. A. 1977. 'Geology of the country around Wells and Cheddar.' *Memoir of the British Geological Survey* (Explanation of Geological Sheet 280).

Harrison, D.J. and Adlam, K.A. McL. 1985. 'The limestone and dolomite resources of the Peak District of Derbyshire and Staffordshire.' *Miner. Assess. Rep. Brit. Geol. Surv.* No. 144.

Harrison, D.J., Hudson, J.M. and Cannell, B. 1991. 'Appraisal of high-purity limestones in England and Wales.' Part 1 Resources. *British Geological Survey Technical Report WF/90/10*. Department of the Environment.

Harrison, D.J. 1992. 'Industrial Minerals Laboratory Manual: Limestone.' *British Geological Survey Technical Report WG/92/29*.

Harrison, D.J., Buckley, D.K. and Marks, R.J. 1992. 'Limestone resources and hydrogeology of the Mendips Hills'. *British Geological Survey Technical Report WA/92/19*.

Kellaway, G. A. and Welch, F. 1993. 'Geology of the Bristol district.' *Memoir of the British Geological Survey*. (Explanation of Bristol Special Geological Sheet).

Rendel, Palmer and Tritton, 1988. *Outline study of the Magnesian Limestone in the UK*. Department of the Environment.

Whitbread, M., Marsay, A. and Tunnell, C. 1991. 'The occurrence and utilisation of mineral and construction wastes.' *Arup Economics and Planning*. HMSO.

HYDROLOGY AND GEOMORPHOLOGY OF LIMESTONE TERRANES, AND THE EFFECTS OF QUARRYING

Peter Smart
Department of Geography, University of Bristol

INTRODUCTION

In Britain limestone terranes have a high landscape value, as recognised by their scheduling as Areas of Outstanding Natural Beauty (for instance the Mendip Hills) and National Parks, such as those of the Peak District and Yorkshire Dales (Figure 9). This high value arises from their topographic eminence, even soft limestones such as the chalk of South East England rising above the adjacent clay lowlands with steep scarp slopes such as those of the North Downs at Reigate. The Carboniferous limestone also forms prominent high areas in the Mendip Hills, Derbyshire and Yorkshire, often incised by spectacular steep-sided gorges such as Cheddar Gorge in Somerset and Goredale Scar in Yorkshire. The thin soils of these uplands were often exploited by early man, whose remains are sometimes preserved in cave deposits, such as those of Charterhouse Warren Farm Swallet near Cheddar (Levitan et. al. 1988, Stanton 1989). These stony soils are not well-suited to intensive arable cultivation, and the charm of areas such as the Yorkshire Dales is in part that they are still relatively wild.

Caves are a particular feature of hard limestones such as the Carboniferous limestone, and their splendours attract both the tourist, and the interests of the sporting caver (Plate 3). Scientifically caves have a particular importance because when abandoned by their formative streams, they accumulate sediments and other deposits from the surface, which are then preserved from subaerial erosion. Using modern techniques such as uranium series analysis, these deposits can be dated (Smart and Francis 1991, Atkinson and Rowe 1992) and the environmental conditions at the time of deposition can be interpreted by analysis of the sediments and their contained flora and fauna. Paradoxically, quarrying has exposed many such deposits for scientific examination before their inevitable

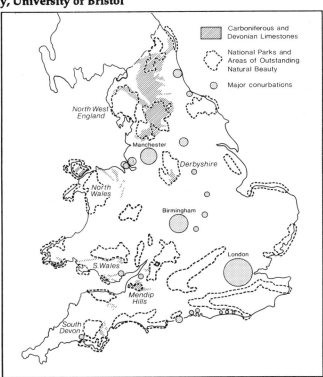

Figure 9 *Distribution of Carboniferous and Devonian limestones in England and Wales in relation to major conurbations, National Parks and Areas of Outstanding Natural Beauty (AONB). The AONB on the North and South Downs (south of London) and Chilterns (west of London) are developed on soft chalk limestones, while the Cotswolds AONB (north-north east of the Mendip Hills) is underlaid by Jurassic limestones.*

destruction. The important Middle Pleistocene site at Westbury-sub-Mendip Quarry (Bishop 1982), which has more fossil mammal species than any other site in Europe, is a very good example.

Stone has been quarried in limestone areas over much of historic time, both for agricultural lime, and for house building. Indeed, the distinctive architectural style of many areas is related to the specific building stones employed, the honeyed limestones of the Cotswolds being a particular example. The problem nowadays arises from the greatly increased rates of abstraction during this century, both in response to local demand, and from the increasing use of aggregates for construction purposes in the South East of England. Modern superquarries such as those in the eastern Mendips (Plate 4), with a production of 5M tonnes per year, are extensive and have a high potential impact on the environment.

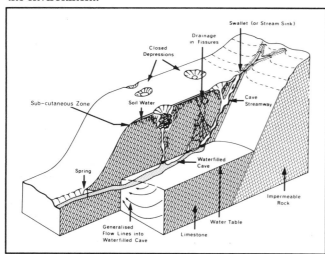

Figure 10 Block diagram of the hydrology of a typical Mendip limestone spring system. Note stream sink with air-filled cave formed at the boundary of the limestones, and shafts draining depressions, which are tributary to the main waterfilled cave conduit. Adjacent to the conduit diffuse flow occurs in fractures and fissures which provide groundwater storage, but significant water is also stored at shallow depth in the subcutaneous zone. Modified after Smith et. al. (1977).

GROUNDWATER HYDROLOGY OF THE MENDIP HILLS

The geomorphology and hydrology of limestones differ from those of other rocks because they are susceptible to dissolution by circulating waters. This gives rise to a distinctive terrane type known as karst, recognisable by the presence of specific landforms such as closed depressions, sinking streams, dry valleys and caves, and an almost complete absence of surface flows (Jennings 1984, White 1988, Ford and Williams 1989). Dissolution of limestone is driven primarily by CO_2 generated in the soil by root respiration and bacterial decomposition of organic matter. Dissolution rates are high at the surface, but reduce with depth giving a zone of enhanced near surface porosity - the subcutaneous zone. This zone is important hydro-logically because it permits lateral concentration of sub-surface flow towards preferred vertical fissures (Smart and Friederich 1986). With time these sites develop into closed depressions, drained by vertical shafts leading down through the unsaturated zone (Williams 1985). Water from shaft depressions links at depth to a network of cave passages which conduct water laterally to spring outflows (Figure 10). Such routes often develop on bedding planes, which are generally more laterally continuous than joints. Initially these are relatively restricted (mm wide), but with continuing dissolution they may develop into fissures (cm wide) and, if net inflows are sufficient, into open cave passages termed conduits (Ford 1988, Palmer 1991). In general the karst of the Mendips is more mature (and thus more karstified) in the west and central Mendips (Ford and Stanton 1968), where the limestones have been exposed for an extended time period, than in the eastern Mendips where much of the most extensive stone extraction is concentrated.

Open cave passages may also develop where surface streams formed on impermeable rocks overlying or adjacent to the limestones sink underground (Figure 10). In the Mendips, streams from the old red sandstone and Silurian volcanic rocks, which form the cores of the hills, sink into the Carboniferous limestone at the boundary with the lower limestone shales, forming major cave systems, such as Swildons Hole (Figure 11) (Smith and Drew 1975). Conduits can thus be thought of as underground rivers, and

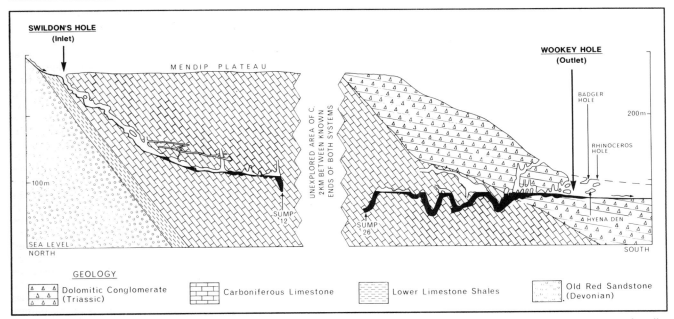

Figure 11 Longitudinal section from Swildons Hole stream sink to Wookey Hole resurgence, central Mendips. Note steep initial descent of swallet stream, followed by water table cave with sumps (short sections of water-filled passage) explored by cavers in Swildons Hole. At Wookey Hole the passage explored by cave divers shows a characteristic looping pattern typical of many water-filled conduits in the Mendips. Note also high level fossil cave at both resurgence and sink, the former preserving significant archaeological and faunal remains.

like surface channels are widely spaced and structured into a dendritic pattern. Conduit flow is rapid and turbulent, with short residence times (Figure 12) and little or no filtration to purify underground waters (Smith et al 1976). Contamination by waste disposal, accidental spillage or by high sediment loads is therefore a problem (Quinlan et. al. 1991, Field 1992). On the Mendips, where many springs are used for supply by Bristol Water, water tracing has been used to define underground catchments, a first step in the protection and management of karst groundwaters. A particular feature of conduits in the Mendips, where the limestones dip to north and south from the folded anticlinal cores which form the crest of the hills, is that they pass rapidly down below the level of adjacent impermeable rocks such as the Keuper marl, which underlies much of the

lowland surrounding the hills. This controls the standing water level or water table within the limestones. Thus fissures and cave passages below this level are completely water-filled, and circulation may occur by pressure flow, sometimes rising vertically up joints to reach the outlet from the limestones, and giving a characteristic looping, long profile (Ford and Ewers 1978) well seen in resurgence cave systems explored by cave divers, such as Wookey Hole (Figure 11). Water tracing evidence suggests that most Mendip conduits are of this type (Stanton and Smart 1981), reaching depths of 60 to 100 m below the water table.

The continuing flow from springs into the summer and through droughts (generally known as base-flow) is sustained by groundwater storage (Figure 13). Although the majority of water discharging from springs is supplied

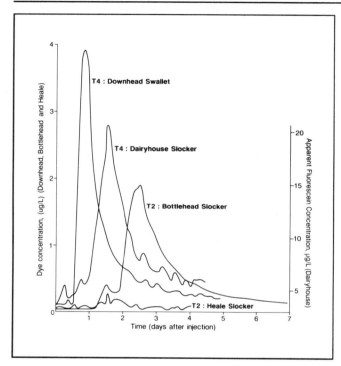

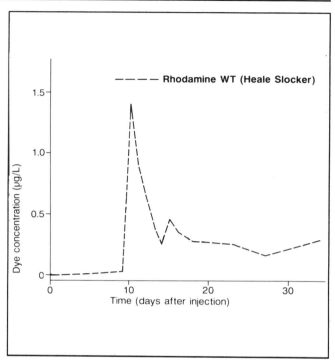

Figure 12(a) Time/concentration curves for dye tracers injected at four main swallets feeding Seven Springs, East Mendip. Sink to rising distance is 2km or less, and the rapid travel times and peaked shape of the curves indicate that flow is in conduits. Prior to sub-water development of the adjacent Torr Quarry, Heale Slocker also fed Seven Springs. Since lowering of the water table this conduit has become non-functional, and tracer now moves from the conduit through the diffuse flow zone to the sump. Figure 12(b) Note the much slower travel times and dispersed nature of the tracer curve.

via conduits, their storage is negligibly small (Atkinson 1977).   Base-flow storage occurs below the water table in water-filled fissures and fractures, which form a constricted ramifying network in the blocks of limestone between the conduits (Figure 10).   This network fills during the winter with a rise in the water table associated with high rainfall (recharge), and drains during the following summer, feeding water into the main conduits.   Circulation is not restricted to the seasonally inundated part of the aquifer, but may extend to considerable depth.   Because of the large number and small size of the fissure and fracture openings, residence times are long (Figure 12b), and flow is laminar.

Thus water quality is good and this part of the aquifer is much less susceptible to pollution than the conduit system (Friederich et. al. 1982).   Unfortunately, it is generally not possible to abstract this water for supply because the rates of transmission are too low to support even low pumping rates from boreholes (Smart and Hobbs 1986).   For this reason groundwater abstraction in the Mendips is almost entirely from the natural outflow of springs.   Some storage of water also occurs in the unsaturated zone, which is particularly deep (>100m) in the Mendips.   The solutionally developed subcutaneous zone is especially important and provides sustained flow for cave drips, which feed the main

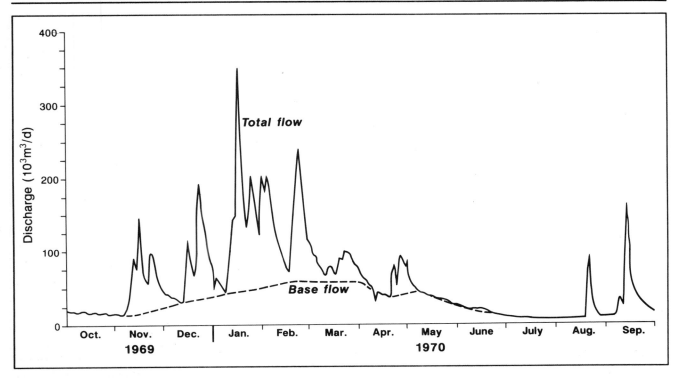

Figure 13   Average daily flow at Cheddar Spring for 1969 and 1970. High flows are associated with storm rainfall in the winter and recharge the aquifer storage, to provide continued discharge during the dry summer months when evaporation exceeds rainfall (after Atkinson 1977).

conduits. Experimental studies suggest that up to 50% of the annual storage in the Mendip limestones may occur in the unsaturated zone (Smart and Friederich 1986, Friederich et. al. 1982).

EFFECTS OF QUARRYING ON WATER RESOURCES

Historically the most significant impact of quarrying on groundwater resources has been pollution due to accidental spillages, for instance of diesel oil, and from suspended sediment generated from the plant area and working floor of the quarry by run off in wet weather. Persistent pollution led to the abandonment of Ashwick Rising as a source by Bristol Water, while Fairy Cave Quarries (Figure 14), which intersected several beautiful fossil caves and an open streamway leading to St Dunstan's Well, was eventually closed. The risk of groundwater pollution can be substantially reduced by adoption of good management practices such as the provision of oil interceptors on drainage from storage tanks and workshop areas, and settling lagoons prior to discharge of runoff to surface streams. However, as in any industrial operation, some risk must remain. Until recently the depth of most Mendip quarries has been limited, to avoid intersection of the water

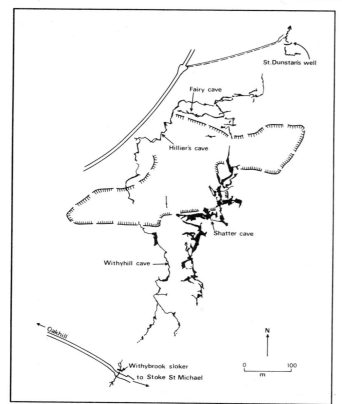

Figure 14 Caves in Fairy Cave Quarry near Stoke St Michael, eastern Mendips. Quarrying (outlined) between the stream sink at Withybrook Slocker and the resurgence (St Dunstan's Well) has intercepted several major fossil cave passages. Of the total of 4,575 m of cave passage entered, 840 m were destroyed by quarrying before the quarries were finally abandoned in 1977. Currently access to these caves is prohibited by the present owners Hobbs Holdings.

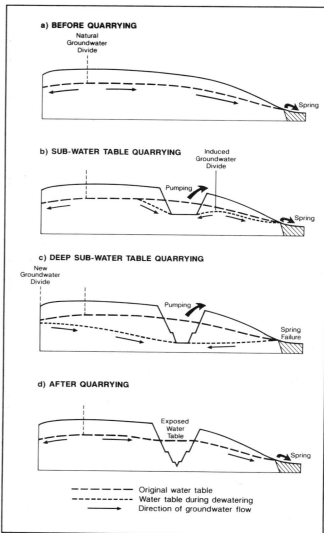

Figure 15 Schematic diagram showing the effect of sub-water table quarrying on groundwater levels in a limestone aquifer (after Harrison et. al. 1992).

table and loss of groundwater by pumping to de-water the limestones prior to working (Somerset County Council 1972, 1974). This policy has been only partially successful because it is now recognised that substantial storage occurs in the unsaturated zone which is lost by quarrying. There may also be an effect on groundwater recharge via disruption of the 'feeders' in the unsaturated zone, and by pumping of runoff ponding on the quarry floor directly into surface rivers. Furthermore, this policy has resulted in lateral expansion of quarries with a resulting loss of land.

More recently, there has been a cautious move to sub-water table quarrying, particularly in the preferred eastern Mendip area, where the unsaturated zone is less thick than in the Central Mendips. Pumping from a sump installed in the lowest quarry level (Plate 5) gives a reduction of water levels within the aquifer (Figure 15), with an increase in the hydraulic gradient in the upstream groundwater flow path, and initially flattening then reversal in the downstream segment (Figure 16). There is an inevitable loss of saturated groundwater storage, which may be increased if transmissive conduits are also directly intersected. As demonstrated by water tracing, reduction of water levels may also result in the conduit becoming non-functional (Figure 12a). There is insufficient head to drive water over the loop crests in the conduit, and slow leakage from the conduit into the quarry via the diffuse flow zone occurs (Figure 12b). This may result in significant regional effects on groundwater flow, with reduction of both peak and base-flows and eventually the drying up of springs (Figure 17). Although, with careful monitoring, water derived from quarry dewatering could be put into supply, there is an inevitable disruption of groundwater flow and loss of resource during sub-water table quarrying. However, on abandonment, there will be a slow recovery of groundwater levels (Figure 15), with substantial storage in the flooded quarry void. This gives a long term change in the dynamics of groundwater flow, significantly attenuating seasonal changes, but offers potential for managed storage and supply.

There is agreement in the quarrying and water industries as to the general effects of quarry development on ground water resources. However, two specific technical problems affect our ability to predict these effects precisely in a specific area. Firstly, because limestones form hetero-geneous aquifers (Smart et. al. 1991), and have very different storage and transmission properties in the conduit and diffuse flow components, their behaviour is not readily represented by the generally available numerical groundwater flow models, which assume homogeneous

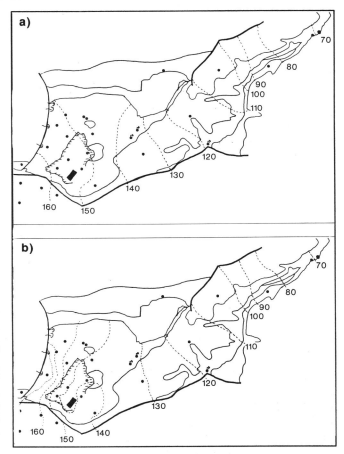

Figure 16 Winter water table contours for the Carboniferous limestone aquifer in the vicinity of Torr Quarry (hatched), East Mendip in 1986 prior to sub-water table development (a) and in 1990 after pumping had commenced (b). Water level contours determined from boreholes (black circles) fall from stream sinks along the western boundary towards Seven Springs on Whatley Brook (centre, black circle with arrowhead), and then eastwards towards Oldford Borehole, a Bristol water source (after Allan Edwards 1993).

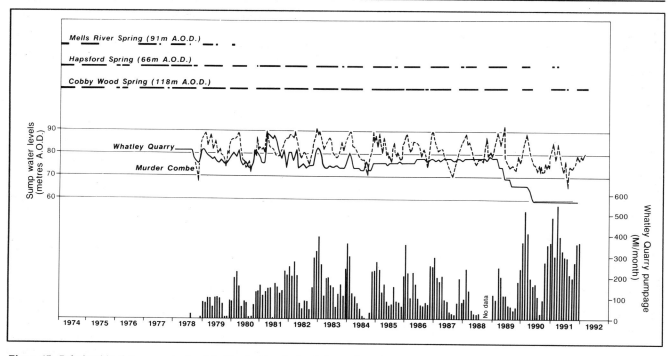

Figure 17 Relationships between water level in Murder Coombe borehole, outflow of Mells River Sink (a reversing spring or estevalle which at low flows functions as a sink) Cobby Wood and Hapsford Springs, which are affected by progressively increased pumping from Whatley Quarry, eastern Mendips. Note that Mells River Sink ceased to discharge after pumping started in 1979, and that both Hapsford Spring (downstream) and Cobby Wood spring (upstream) were also affected when the quarry sump was deepened in 1989. This also affected the water level in the Murder Coombe borehole adjacent to the quarry (after Stanton 1993, proof of evidence to Whatley Quarry Planning Enquiry).

conditions (Teutsch and Sauter 1991). Secondly, even if appropriate models are developed, we are unable to predict the position or geometry of the conduits, which are the major transmission routes for groundwater flow in mature karst areas and which control water levels in the adjacent diffuse flow blocks, either from general theory or from geophysical or other site investigation techniques. The same is also true of the fossil cave passages which have a high earth science and sporting interest. Thus although we recognise the direct impact of quarries on the environment (Department of the Environment 1991), for instance in the intersection and destruction of caves, the prediction of these effects is difficult, and there also remains considerable uncertainty as to the hydrological effects of sub-water table quarry development, and its long term effects.

REFERENCES

Atkinson, T.C. 1977. 'Diffuse flow and conduit flow in a limestone terrain in the Mendip Hills, England.' *Journal of Hydrology*, 35, 93–110.

Atkinson, T.C. and Smart, P.L. 1981. 'Artificial tracers in hydrogeology.' In *A Summary of British Hydrogeology - 1980*, The Royal Society, 173-190.

Atkinson, T.C. and Rowe, P.J. 1992. 'Applications of dating to denudation chronology and landscape evolution.' In Ivanovich, M. and Harmon, R.S. *Uranium Series Disequilibrium*. Oxford, 669-703.

Bishop, M.J. 1982. 'The mammal fauna of the early middle Pleistocene cavern infill site of Westbury-Sub-Mendip, Somerset.' *Palaeontological Association Special Paper*, 28, 1-108.

Edwards, A.J. and Smart, P.L. 1989. 'Waste disposal on karstified Carboniferous Limestone of England and Wales.' In Beck, B.F. *Engineering and Environmental Impacts of Sinkholes and Karst*. Balkema, Rotterdam, 165-182.

Department of the Environment 1991. *Environmental Effects of Surface Mineral Workings*, HMSO.

Field, M.S. 1992. 'Karst hydrology and chemical contamination.' *Journal of Environmental Systems* 22, 1-26.

Ford, D.C. and Stanton, W.I. 1968. 'Geomorphology of the south-central Mendip Hills.' *Proceedings of the Geological Association* 79, 401-427.

Ford, D.C. and Ewers, R.O. 1978. 'The development of limestone cave systems in the dimensions of length and depth.' *Canadian Journal of Earth Sciences* 15, 1783-1798.

Ford, D.C. 1988. 'Characteristics of dissolutional cave systems in carbonate rocks.' In James, N.P. and Choquette, P.W. *Paleokarst*, Springer Verlag, 25-57.

Ford, D.C. and Williams, P.W. 1989. *Karst Geomorphology and Hydrology*, Unwin Hyman.

Friederich, H., Smart, P.L. and Hobbs, R.P. 1982. 'The microflora of limestone percolation water and its implications for limestone springs.' *Transactions of the British Cave Research Association* 9, 15-26.

Harrison, D.J., Buckley, D.K. and Malks, R.J. 1992. 'Limestone resources and hydrogeology of the Mendip Hills.' *British Geological Survey Technical Report*, WA/92/19.

Jennings, J.N. 1984. *Karst*. MIT Press.

Levitan, B.M., Audsley, A., Hawkes, C.J., Moody, A., Moody, P., Smart, P.L. and Thomas, J.S. 1988. 'Charterhouse Warren Farm Swallet, Mendip, Somerset. Exploration, geomorphology, taphonomy and archaeology.' *Proceedings of the University of Bristol Speleological Society*, 18, 171-239.

Palmer, A.N. 1991. 'Origin and morphology of limestone caves.' *Bulletin of the Geological Society of America*, 103, 1-21.

Quinlan, J. et. al. 1991. 'Recommended administrative regulatory definition of karst aquifer, principles for classification of karst aquifers, and practical evaluation of vulnerability of karst aquifers.' *Proceedings of the 3rd Conference on Hydrogeology and Management of Groundwater in Karst Terrains*, National Water Well Association, 573-635.

Smith, D.I. and Drew, D.P. 1975. *The Limestones and Caves of the Mendip Hills*. David and Charles.

Smith, D.I., Atkinson, T.C. and Drew, D.P. 1976. 'The hydrology of limestone terrains.' In Ford, T.D. and Cullingford, C.H.D., *The Science of Speleology*, Academic Press, 179-212.

Smart, P.L. and Hobbs, S.L. 1986. 'Characterisation of carbonate aquifers: a conceptual base.' *Proceedings of the Conferences on Environmental Problems of Karst Terrains and their Solutions*, National Water Well Association, 2-14.

Smart, P.L. and Frances, P.D. 1991. *Quaternary Dating Methods - a User's Guide*, Quaternary Research Association.

Smart, P.L. and Friederich, H. 1986. 'Water movement and storage in the unsaturated zone of a maturely karstified carbonate aquifer, Mendip Hills, England.' *Proceedings of the Conferences on Environmental Problems of Karst Terrains and their Solution*, National Water Well Association, 59-87.

Smart, P.L., Edwards, A.J. and Hobbs, S.L. 1991. 'Heterogeneity in carbonate aquifers: effects of scale, fissuration, lithology and karstification.' *Proceedings of the 3rd Conference on Hydrogeology and Management of Ground Water in Karst Terrains*, National Water Well Association, 373-388.

Somerset County Council 1972. *Quarrying in Somerset, and Draft Policy for Quarrying* (1974).

Stanton, W.I. and Smart, P.L. 1981. 'Repeated dye traces of underground streams in the Mendip Hills, Somerset.' *Proceedings of the University of Bristol Speleological Society,* 16, 47-58.

Stanton, W.I. 1989. 'Beaker age deposits on Mendip at Charterhouse Warren Farm Swallet and Bos Swallet.' *Proceedings of the University of Bristol Speleological Society,* 18, 395-399.

Teutsch, G. and Sauter, M. 1991. 'Groundwater modeling in karst terranes: scale effects, data acquisition and field validation.'

Proceedings of the 3rd Conference on Hydrogeology, Ecology, Monitoring and Management of Ground Water in Karst Terrains. National Water Well Association, 17-35.

White, W.B. 1988. *Geomorphology and Hydrology of Karst Terrains.* Oxford University Press.

Williams, P.W. 1985. 'Subcutaneous hydrology and the development of doline and cockpit karst.' *Zeitschrift fur Geomorphologie* N.F. 29, 463-482.

THE CASE FOR THE LIMESTONE ENVIRONMENT

Willie Stanton,
Westbury-sub-Mendip, Wells, Somerset

INTRODUCTION

Letter to the Editor, *Wells Journal,* 24th February 1967

Sir — The photograph of the 1906 landslide at New Quarry in Cheddar Gorge, published in your edition of January 27th, makes me wonder what would have become of the Gorge had this providential slide not taken place. It seems all too likely that our magnificent Gorge would, like Shipham Combe nearby, have been utterly ruined for the millions of visitors it now receives each year.

The Mendip quarries today are such enormous concerns, with such tremendous potential for transforming beautiful scenery into industrial wasteland, that the choice of new sites for quarrying demands a deep sense of public responsibility on the part of quarry companies as well as planning departments...

I wrote this letter standing under a holm oak tree in Portugal. It was my 14th year as geologist to a Portuguese mining firm, a time when I came home to the Mendips at 3-year intervals. This meant that the expansion of the quarries was perhaps more obvious and shocking to me than to local people who watched them grow imperceptibly, day by day.

I had already completed a study of the Mendip quarries (Stanton 1966) which covered their history and their effects on those special features of limestone country: spectacular scenery, caves and underground water. Already the Mendips had lost more than a mile of cave passage to quarries. Escarpments and combes had been scarred, and springs used for public water supply had been polluted. Yet the rate of stone extraction was only about 6M tonnes in 1966, compared to more than 13 Mt per year today.

Looking back, it is hard to credit how little we realised, in the years after the Second World War, how the quarry industry would expand. Huge concessions were granted by local councils in the late 1940s on the assumption that small quarries could be developed here and there within them. Instead, in many cases, the whole concession was devoured and the quarry operators came back for more.

We were also profoundly ignorant, in those days, of the nature of the Carboniferous limestone aquifer, that great rocky sponge that supplies up to 90 billion litres of drinking water to Bristol, Somerset and Avon each year and provides an equal quantity to the rivers Axe, Yeo, Mells, Chew, Banwell and other smaller streams that rise in the Mendips. One school of thought even held that there was no water table under Mendip.

From the 1970s onward dozens of research boreholes were drilled, first by the Bristol Avon River Authority and the Wessex Water Authority and later by quarry firms. Bristol University geographers pioneered the tracing of underground streams using fluorescent dyes and the spores of a club moss, and Wessex Water Authority and the Wessex Cave Club carried the work forward until more than 90 underground connections had been proved and the catchment areas of all the big Mendip springs could be defined with confidence.

The effects of sub-water-table quarrying on the water table, and on flows in rivers and streams, have now been monitored for 20 years. To claim, as some people still do, that the influence of quarrying on the Mendip water table is not understood, simply demonstrates that those people have not studied the available literature (comprehensively reviewed in Harrison, Buckley and Marks 1992).

Bath City Council joined the investigation after 1977 when 'the bug', an amoeba liable to cause fatal meningitis in humans, was found to be living in the Hot Springs. The Spa was closed following this unwelcome discovery. Research boreholes were drilled and the hydrogeology and hydrothermal output of the Hot Springs have been monitored ever since (Kellaway 1991). Sources of 'bug-free' hot water have now been developed and the high water table in the Carboniferous limestone of the Mendips is known to be essential to the continued well-being of the Hot Springs.

I was fortunate to have been involved in all these investigations. I have also researched into the caves, minerals, mines and landforms of the Mendips, co-authored a reference book (Barrington and Stanton 1977) and written many scientific papers contributing new facts to our knowledge of the Hills.

Fifty years of intimate association with the Mendips, above and below ground, have made me very conscious of how fast their unique character is being destroyed in the name of 'development'. Spreading human occupation and increasingly intensive farming are wiping out rare plants and animals and polluting underground streams and springs. The sport of cave exploring has become so popular that, in spite of the great care taken by most cavers, many once-beautiful stalactite grottoes have degenerated into muddy holes. Above all, the vast quarries have removed hills and valleys, caves and springs, mineral and prehistoric treasures.

The days when small quarries served their own locality, advanced slowly and took enough interest in the caves, mines or archaeological deposits that they encountered to organise 'rescue' operations by experts, are long gone. Small quarries, worked out and reverted to Nature, provided landscape diversity and wildlife habitats. How different are today's vast commercial enterprises which have to ignore, for the sake of cost-effectiveness, the scientific treasures that they expose, shovel up and transport to the waste dumps.

Astonishing coups were achieved, long ago, by the generosity of far-sighted individuals and groups like the Society for the Preservation of Natural Scenery which bought the threatened north side of Cheddar Gorge in 1909 (Hendy 1981) or Wing Commander Hodgkinson of Wookey Hole who bought Ebbor Gorge, equally threatened by a proposed quarry, in 1931. Both properties eventually were gifted to the National Trust.

THE VALUE OF HARD LIMESTONE TO SOCIETY

Hard limestone, such as the Carboniferous limestone of the Mendips, the Yorkshire Dales and the Peak District, serves our daily needs in two distinct and opposite ways. More than any other kind of rock limestone is quarried and crushed to make aggregate for the construction industry. 140 Mt of crushed rock are produced each year in Britain; of this some 90 Mt, or 63%, is limestone (Pollock 1989).

Conversely, also more than any other rock, limestone left in its natural place in the ground provides society with huge renewable water resources for public supply, spectacular scenery for tourism, open space for amenity, caves and inland cliffs for recreation and sport, mines and minerals for science, and archaeological sites for prehistory.

I will argue that hard limestone in situ is so much more valuable to society than the other rocks favoured by quarrymen - granite, gritstone and basalt — that it should only be extracted to serve essential purposes that the other rocks, by their nature, cannot satisfy.

Limestone is basically a chemical, calcium carbonate, that is vital to industries such as steel, chemicals, plastics, drugs, glass, sugar, paper and cement. In agriculture, as lime, it is indispensable. It will neutralise acid fumes from fossil fuel power stations, reclaim acidified water catchments and purify effluent. There is no chemical substitute for calcium carbonate in these fields.

However, only a small proportion, c. 10%, of each year's production of hard limestone aggregate is used for chemical purposes. The great bulk is used by the construction industry for concrete, roadstone, common fill and railway ballast. Other hard rocks would serve these purposes as well, but limestone is preferred largely because it occurs in vast deposits of high purity, closer than other hard rocks to the great markets of South East England. Limestone aggregate is cheap because it is easy to quarry, because it is close to its markets, and because the quarry companies have never been required to compensate society for the special environmental losses associated with the removal of hard limestone hills.

Even the small proportion of hard limestone that is quarried for chemical purposes could be replaced by soft limestone such as chalk. There is not, therefore, any absolute need to quarry hard limestone.

TABLE 9
QUARRIED LIMESTONE HAS THE WIDEST RANGE OF INDUSTRIAL USES

	Hard Limestone		Granite		Basalt		Gritstone	
Cost of Extraction	Low	5	High	2	High	2	V. High	1
Common aggregate	Good	5	Good	5	Good	5	Good	5
Base aggregate	V. Good	5	Good	4	V. Good	5	Good	4
Wearing course	Not Used	0	Medium	3	Good	4	V. Good	5
Quarry wastage	Low	4	Medium	3	High	2	V. High	1
Building stone	Used	2	Useful	3	Rarely used	1	Used	2
Chemical	Yes	5	No	0	No	0	No	0
Extracted stone (total score)		26		20		19		18

Table 9 summarises the values to society of the 4 commonest types of aggregate. Limestone is marginally the most useful, mainly because of its special chemical properties.

However hard limestone in situ, in the ground, is also useful to society in a much greater variety of ways than are the other hard rocks. Table 10 demonstrates how hard limestone stands head and shoulders above its competitors in this respect.

Hard limestones, being slightly soluble in rainwater, develop naturally into the unique landform known as 'karst'. Even in quite low hills, karstic scenery exhibits rugged rocky landscapes with inland cliffs, caves, gorges, sinkholes, great springs, potholes, dry surface valleys and underground rivers. In Britain the Carboniferous limestone forms internationally famous features such as Cheddar Gorge, Gaping Ghyll pothole and the Hot Springs of Bath. The huge caves and rugged gorges of Central France and Slovenia, the underground glaciers of the Austrian Alps and above all the remote regions of Southern China, where the 'stone forests' and vertiginous limestone pillars called tower karst are the acme of limestone scenery, are as fascinating to visitors as snow-capped mountain peaks in Switzerland or the Himalayas.

Limestone aquifers in Britain produce more drinking water than all other aquifers together. Soft limestones such as the chalk are more porous and can store more water, but the hard limestones usually form higher hills and in regions with higher rainfall. The waters resurging from limestone springs are hard with dissolved lime, so their rivers do not suffer from the same acidification problems as those from granite or gritstone catchments.

Non-calcareous rocks break down into peaty, clayey or sandy acidic soils that support a very limited flora. The flora, and hence the fauna, of limy soils is much richer. Limestone soil can nurture the full range of both lime-loving and lime-hating plants, from bee orchid, rock rose and Cheddar pink to rhododendrons and foxgloves, within a few square metres: the former where the soil is thin, and the latter where it is thick and percolating rainwater has leached away the lime.

Above ground in many limestone regions the thin soils

TABLE 10
RELATIVE VALUES OF QUARRY FEEDROCKS WHEN LEFT IN THE GROUND

	Hard Limestone		Granite		Basalt		Gritstone	
Aquifer	Good	4	Poor	1	Poor	1	Occassional	2
Landscape	V. Good	5	V. Good	5	Good	4	V. Good	5
Attractions (examples in the British Isles)	Cheddar Gorge Bath Hot Springs Wookey Hole Caves Malham Cave and Burren Pavements	5	Dartmoor tors Land's End and Lundy Island	4	Giant's Causeway Fingal's Cave and High Force	4	Pen-y-Fan Croagh-Patrick and Suilven	4
Speleology	Yes	5	No	0	No	0	No	0
Walking, climbing	V. Good	5	V. Good	5	Good	4	V. Good	5
Open Space	Yes	5	Yes	5	Yes	4	Yes	5
Paleolithic remains	Many	5	Many	5	Few	1	Few	1
Mines, minerals	Many	5	Many	5	Few	1	Few	1
Agricultural soil	Good	4	Poor	2	V.Good	5	Poor	2
Fauna and flora	V. Diverse	5	Limited	2	Good	4	Limited	2
In situ stone (total score)		48		29		27		26

and rocky outcrops do not favour intensive farming. Such areas have often become unrestricted open space, used by the public for walking, picnicking, flying kites and similar pastimes. Below ground the cave systems exceed 7 km in the Mendips and 20 km in length in Wales and the Pennines. The expeditions into their furthest recesses, though taking place only an hour's drive from city centres, demand as much discipline, skill and endurance as expeditions to scale Alpine peaks by the more difficult routes. Uniquely, in this age when all seems to be known, cave explorers can still savour the strange experience of being the first to set foot in great silent halls under the hills, their eyes the first to see the richly coloured tapestries of crystalline stalactites and stalagmites - but only in hard limestone. Cave exploring, or speleology, is a combined sport and science that has tens of thousands of devotees in Britain (Plate 3).

The prehistory of a land and its inhabitants is largely deciphered by the study of ancient bones, stone tools and other materials preserved in limestone caves, those treasure houses of days gone by. Deposits more than a million years old can be dated by uranium-series absolute age determinations on cave stalagmite.

The extreme geological processes to which the older limestones have been subjected have hardened and mineralised them. Mines for lead, zinc, iron, copper, barytes, ochre, umber, fluorspar and other minerals in the Mendips and Pennines have mostly ceased working, but some of them are still accessible and are exciting to explore and study.

ENVIRONMENTAL LOSS CAUSED BY QUARRIES ON THE MENDIP HILLS

Large-scale quarrying of Mendip limestone began in about 1870, when bulk transport by rail became possible. Before then the stone had been worked in scores of small local pits for walling, lime burning, buildings and turnpike roads. Earlier still, the Mendips had lost about 28,000 tonnes of limestone each year by natural processes, dissolved by percolating rainwater and discharged from the springs as hard water.

The tonnage of limestone quarried from Mendip first exceeded the tonnage carried away in streams at some time in the nineteenth century. Now the human erosion rate has reached more than 600 times the natural rate.

The greatest impact has been on Mendip scenery. A small hill at Vobster has disappeared. Larger hills at Sandford, Milton and Dulcote, featuring prominently in the settings of the Winscombe Valley and the city of Wells, have lost up to two-thirds of their substance. Quarries near Cheddar have destroyed the rocky valleys of Shipham Gorge, Batts Combe and Chelms Combe. Nearby dry valleys have been levelled by filling with quarry waste. In East Mendip, where quarrying has concentrated, more than 20% of the limestone outcrop is consented for quarrying and 9 deep valleys have already suffered major damage. Torr Quarry near Frome is totally remodelling half a square mile of countryside; the vast hole is surrounded by towering 'environmental banks' that hide it from view.

About 600,000 people in Somerset and Avon get their water supply from the Mendip Hills, which, although comparatively small in area, are high enough to attract an average annual rainfall of 1,000-1,200 millimetres. This is more than in any other part of Southern England east of Exmoor, and in consequence the Mendips provide 40% more water per unit area than any major English aquifer south of the Pennines.

Most Mendip limestone has been extracted from the so-called 'dry' zone above the water table. Actually, the dry zone holds huge volumes of water in temporary storage, seeping down very slowly to the water table. You can see it on its way in the caves, falling one drop at a time from stalactite to stalagmite. Plant life on Mendip doesn't all die in great droughts like that of 1976, even though the water table is 100 metres or more beneath the deepest tree roots, because the plants are kept alive by the water in temporary storage. Nor do the stalactites stop dripping in droughts, only the intervals between drops are longer. When the dry zone is removed, rainfall runs off into rivers with no delay, increasing flood peaks, and there is less stored water to maintain river flow in dry summers. The dry zone is also a purification zone in which polluting matter is filtered, oxygenated and broken down by bacteria, as polluted water finds a way down to the water table.

However in East Mendip increasing tonnages of limestone are being quarried from sub-water table workings that are dewatered by constant pumping. The result is that the water table in the surrounding strata is lowered, reducing or stopping the natural overflow of springs. Quarrying has already shrunk or polluted seven East Mendip springs that once were large and clear: Winter Well, Holwell Spring, St. Dunstan's Well, Mells River Estavelle, Cobby Wood Spring, Seven Springs and Hapsford Spring. The pumped water is also more prone to contamination than was the natural, pre-quarrying, springwater.

Most Mendip quarries began their lives by eating into a limestone cliff or rocky slope, a natural rock garden. When such a quarry is worked out it may be left empty, in which case the natural fauna and flora will slowly return. In other abandoned quarries that have been used as industrial or residential sites, an impoverished limestone flora has reappeared. The third alternative, 'restoring' the quarry by filling it with refuse, eventually develops a flora unrelated to limestone.

Of the c. 1,100 hectares of Mendip limestone outcrop that has been quarried, or is due to be quarried, about one tenth was open space or woodland used by the public for recreation. Many footpaths crossing quarry land have been diverted or stopped. A few old quarries with high vertical faces are used for training by rock climbers, notably the Split Rock Quarry near Wells which dates from the 1940s. In contrast modern quarries favour low sloping faces.

Cave exploration is a form of recreation virtually specific to limestone (Plate 3). Caves have been found and destroyed in most Mendip quarries. At least 1.7 km of recorded cave passages, and an unknown length of caves that escaped the attention of speleologists, have been lost. There is no doubt that all the large caves devoured by quarries would, in time, have been discovered intact by cavers, by excavation with or without geophysical assistance.

In the first half of this century many Mendip quarry owners allowed, even welcomed, scientific study of their cave deposits. Caves with Palaeolithic, Neolithic and Romano-British remains were examined in Uphill, Chelms Combe, Milton, Dulcote and Whatley quarries. However since the 1950s only one quarry cave deposit has been investigated in detail. This was the mass of earth, sand and rock filling a huge cavern in Central Mendip, intersected by Westbury Quarry, which contained rich Cromerian faunas (about half a million years old) including exotic extinct animals such as sabre-tooth tiger, cave bear, cave hyaena and cave lion. Also present were flint tools that are still the oldest known relics of Man in Britain. Yet, despite its importance, and although excavations by the British Museum (Natural History) continued for 7 years, most of the Westbury deposit was blasted away.

One quarry, at Sandford in West Mendip, is located in a Mendip orefield (Stanton 1981). It has engulfed several lead mines of medieval or later date, and its consented area contains many more old workings for lead, ochre and zinc, including the extensive underground systems of Pearl Mine, Sandford Levvy and Triple Hole.

THE MENDIP LIMESTONE BUDGET

The Mendip Hills contain 27 cubic kilometres of hard limestone above sea level. To make this calculation I applied conventional ore-reserve methodology to published geological and Ordnance Survey maps and I believe it to be accurate to better than 5%. This finite limestone resource, amounting to c. 67 billion tonnes, is being used in a variety of ways that can be quantified, more or less crudely, in cash-flow terms.

Quarried limestone is valued in the debit account. The 340 Mt extracted from the Mendips before 1993 were worth about £1,224 million at current ex-quarry prices (taken to average about £3.60 per tonne). On the same basis, sales of limestone aggregate from Mendip quarries grossed about £46 million in 1992.

The credit account, that relates to in situ limestone, is much more complex.

Tourist caves at Cheddar and Wookey Hole attract nearly a million visitors a year who pay about £3 million to see the caves. Much more is spent on food and drink, shopping, transport, accommodation etc. by these visitors as well as by others who come to Cheddar Gorge and the Mendips but do not venture into the caves. A visitor survey by Somerset County Council in 1988 found that spending by transient tourists and day visitors to Mendip and Sedgemoor Districts (which include most of the Mendips) amounted to c. £39 million. Allotting half of this sum to limestone-dependent attractions (a conservative estimate), and allowing for spending by the many longer-stay tourists at Mendip caravan and camp sites, it is reasonable to budget for a tourist income generated by Mendip limestone of £30 million in 1988, equivalent to £36 million in 1992.

The Hot Springs of Bath are fed by water from the Mendips (in a circulation driven by the high Mendip water table) that acquires geothermal heat as it flows through limestone caves beneath the Radstock coalfield at depths exceeding 2 km. There are other Georgian cities and Roman ruins in Britain, but the daily outpouring of 1.4 million litres of water at 45°C is unique in North West Europe (excluding Iceland). The Hot Springs have made Bath into Britain's second most popular tourist centre with a tourism derived cash flow exceeding £120 million; their value to the city may be conservatively assessed at 10% of the total, or £12 million per year.

The importance of the Mendip limestone aquifer can be gauged by the estimated cost of replacing the 90 billion litres of drinking water that it can provide each year by equally good water from elsewhere. The water suppliers consider that a new water source on this scale would have to be the River Severn, at a cost of c. £24 million per year running costs plus amortised capital costs.

Add to these figures the spending by cave explorers, who make about 50,000 visits to underground Mendip each year, and by rock climbers, and the annual cash-flow from in situ Mendip limestone totals about £73 million.

Crook's Peak in the Mendip Hills Area of Outstanding Natural Beauty.

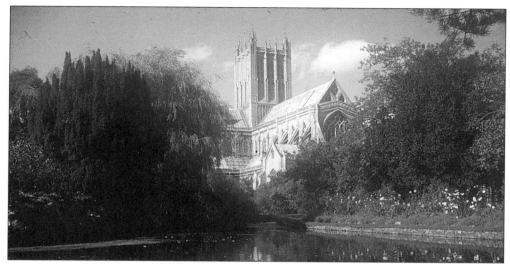

Wells Cathedral. Hills featuring prominently in the setting of the City of Wells have lost two thirds of their substance due to limestone quarrying. Ironically significant parts of the Cathedral are constructed of local limestone. (Courtesy of Willie Stanton).

Landscaping of a quarry site.

That is an estimate of the tangible trading value. It ignores the existence of intangible matters such as the Mendip Area of Outstanding Natural Beauty, which cannot be valued in cash terms, although the importance of protected 'green lung' areas to the fast-growing urban populations of the West Country is obvious. Another significant intangible is the fact that famous limestone attractions draw many foreign tourists, and their hard currency, to Britain. The Michelin tourist guide, *England — The West Country*, lists only 5 principal sights that can be said to depend on their constituent rock. Two are specifically Mendip limestone (Cheddar Gorge and Wookey Hole Caves) but the other 3 (Dartmoor, Exmoor, Bodmin Moor) are more loosely linked to granite and other rocks.

The intangibles associated with quarried limestone are mostly of negative value. Noise, traffic hazards, dust in dry weather and mud in wet, water pollution, bright lights at night, devaluation of property, loss of open space, wildlife habitats and local amenity — all cause distress to people living near quarries and on the lorry access routes. 'Amenity banks' surround some quarries and succeed in hiding not only the quarry but also the rest of the landscape. One matter can be costed: roads subject to pounding by 38-tonne lorries need to be improved. Bypasses and relief roads have been built to divert the juggernauts around Frome, Warminster and Trowbridge. The road costs and capital charges are assessed at about £3 million per year.

On an annual cash-flow basis it can be argued that the value of quarried Mendip limestone in 1992 (£46 million less negative intangibles and £3 million road charges) was very much less than the value of in situ Mendip limestone (£73 million plus positive intangibles). Annual comparisons are, however, misleading because the demand for aggregate is so variable. In 1988 the budget may have nearly balanced. To obtain a truer picture we need to budget for the total limestone resource of the Mendip Hills - 67 billion tonnes.

At the 1992 extraction rate of 12.8 Mt, worth £46 million, the resource would be used up in 5,230 years. At the natural wastage rate of 28,000 tonnes per year, with each in situ year worth £73 million, the resource would last for 2.4 million years (and if sea levels continued to fall at geologically recent rates there would still be Mendip-sized

limestone hills at the end of the period). On this basis the Mendips are worth £240 billion as limestone aggregate and £175 trillion, 730 times as much, as limestone hills.

The budget is simplistic, but its overall good sense is illustrated by the economics of a particular Mendip quarry. Fairy Cave Quarry near Shepton Mallet closed in 1977 having produced 4.5 Mt of limestone in its 35 years of life. The average annual value of the quarry was £0.5 million. It broke into and destroyed stalactite caves of exceptional beauty which, had they been opened to the public on the same basis as Wookey Hole and Cheddar Caves, could hardly have failed to generate a cash-flow exceeding £1 million per year into the indefinite future. The goose that could have laid golden eggs was crippled (not killed, because some caves still survive in the quarry).

The limestone budget is not complete until its implications for employment are considered. Quarrying is increasingly capital-intensive. In 1969, when Mendip limestone production was about 8 Mt, the jobs of some 2,700 people depended on the quarries. In 1988, with production doubled (Figure 18), the number of jobs was about the

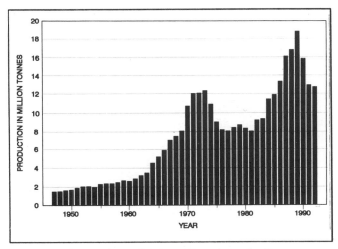

Figure 18 Annual Somerset limestone production.

same. By contrast, Mendip-based tourism, recreation and water supply are labour-intensive occupations employing growing numbers of people (estimated at 5,000 in 1992).

It is self-evident that quarrying hard limestone on a massive scale is a short-term expedient for which, in the long term, the nation will pay dearly. Why then do we continue to exploit our local hard limestone resource at 1/730th of its true value? As with many other finite resources, the explanation is that it is cheap now, and future generations can look after themselves.

Critics of the limestone budget have suggested a 'compromise' whereby, given that most of the credit account is generated by tourism, quarries should be allowed to remove all the limestone except for the main tourist attractions like Cheddar Gorge, Burrington Combe and Wookey Hole. There are short term and long term answers to this idea.

The short term answer points out that the water resource, the caves, the archaeology, the limestone scenery and the minerals are not confined to these main tourist areas but are dispersed from end to end of the Mendips. Nor is it known which parts of the hills feed water to the Hot Springs of Bath. It is a fact that if their flow or heat output were once reduced by quarrying there can be no certainty that cessation of quarrying would then entirely restore the natural flow and temperature. The Hot Springs depend on the high Mendip water table, and the bigger the quarry, the less the water table will recover when the quarry finally stops pumping.

The long term answer takes note of the fact that Cheddar Gorge, Wookey Hole, Ebbor Gorge, Burrington Combe, Bath Hot Springs and all the lesser scenic attractions were developed from nothing, while the Mendip Hills were being raised up by geological processes. The time-span involved, one to two million years, is short by geological standards (dinosaurs ruled the earth for 50 times as long). Leave the limestone in situ and in due course new caves, gorges, water resources and karst scenery will form to take the place of today's money-spinning assets. Remove the limestone and no regeneration is possible, ever.

Why worry about so distant a future? In the next section I touch on the consequences of having no concern for even the near future.

PREDICTING FUTURE DEMANDS FOR MENDIP LIMESTONE

Twenty-two years ago I wrote in *Man and the Mendips* (Mendip Society, 1971) that the then rapid growth in demand for aggregates reflected the phenomenal expansion of those times, the building of new or wider roads and new or larger towns. 'Any halt or reversal in the growth of this country's population or prosperity, or both, would slow down or reverse the growth in the national need for stone.'

The graph (Figure 18) shows how Mendip limestone production increased by a factor of 8 between 1947 and 1992. The underlying trend is a steady rise, which corresponds to an English population increase of 7.3 million over the period (Office of Population Censuses and Surveys statistics) coupled with an overall increase in prosperity from post-war austerity to the present day. Superimposed on the underlying trend are strong fluctuations in demand that represent short term prosperity changes: the economic boom years of the 1960s, the early 1970s and the mid 1980s, separated by the post 1973 and post 1988 depressions. England's population grew steadily at roughly 160,000 per year over the period of the graph, except for the decade 1973-1983 when growth was small (OPCS statistics). On this basis I can reasonably claim that developments in the demand for stone have been entirely in line with my predictions.

Population growth of c. 160,000 per year necessitates building, each year, the equivalent of two new cities the size of Bath, with all the required infrastructure such as new or wider roads throughout the country. The relevance of population growth to the demand for construction aggregate is obvious (although other factors, such as the decreasing size of the average household and the increase in car ownership per family, add to the overall requirement).

What of the future? It is customary to forecast changes a few decades ahead by extrapolating selected trends of the recent past. Thus the perceived recent growth in Britain's population and prosperity has led to official predictions of a continuous steep rise in construction activity, and thus in the demand for aggregates, during the period to 2011 (Department of the Environment 1993). For England and Wales, the predicted increase is from 240 Mt of aggregates

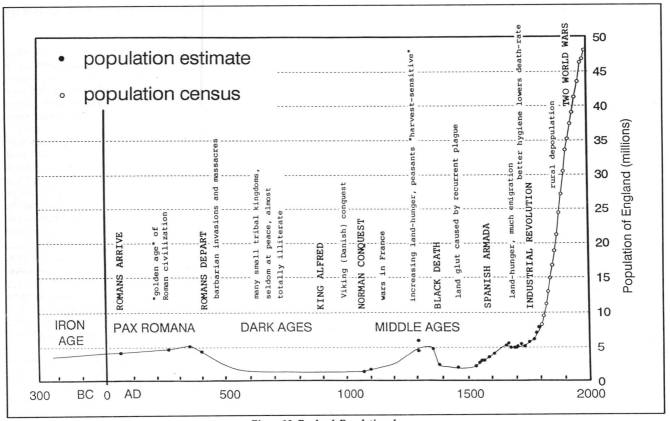

Figure 19 England: Population change.

in 1991 to 410 Mt in 2011. For Mendip limestone, the predicted increase would seem to be from 13 Mt in 1991 to more than 30 Mt in 2011. (Compare this to the figure of c.20 Mt in 2011 obtained by extrapolating the average growth rate, 1947-1992, deduced from Figure 18).

In reality, there is no precedent for such sustained rapid growth over a full 20 year period, and the fragility of these amazing predictions is shown by the fact that they are 10% less than predictions made by the same consultants only one year previously, in 1991 (Department of the Environment 1993, page 7).

Why are these predictions so unbelievable? In the first place, many authorities argue that Britain has not experienced real economic growth since 1972, the so-called boom of the 1980s having been largely credit-financed. Now, after 20 years of economic stagnation, the country finds itself with huge deficits in its external balance of trade and its internal budget, as well as a falling share of world trade. The next boom, if it comes, is likely to be based more on wishful thinking than on sound finances.

The graph (Figure 19) is relevant to the link between population change and the demand for aggregate. It shows how English populations have twice suffered sudden catastrophic reductions in historic times, first by barbarian massacres following the breakdown of Roman civilisation, and second by the onslaught of a fatal plague that was ideally suited to the social conditions of the fourteenth century.

The runaway population growth of the last 250 years, nurtured by scientific and technical innovation, has created a crowded highly complex society that is difficult to govern.

Clever life-prolonging medical practice has produced an aging population that the state is struggling to support. Sophisticated automation has led to mass unemployment. It seems, therefore, that unrestrained innovation can be self-defeating. As population density increases, so does the power of each ethnic, religious or political lobby. The result is a discontented divided society in which more and more people resort to antisocial behaviour to get their own way. Only one defence, the rule of law, protects such a society from a new Dark Age.

On the world scale (Figure 20) populations passed the

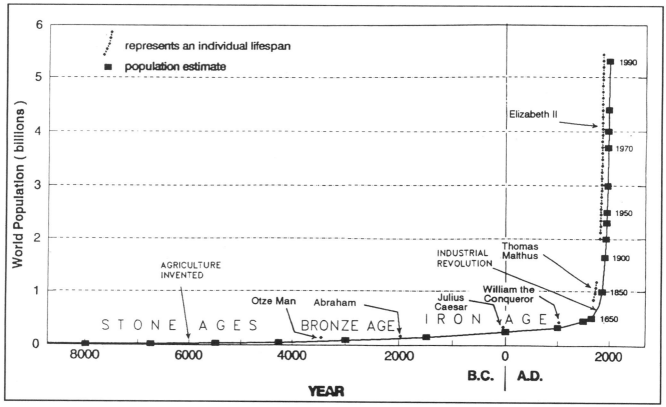

Figure 20 World population growth.

sustainable good quality of life mark of about 1 billion in 1850. World population could reach the 10 billion mark, thought by some demographers to be the absolute (unsustainable) planetary maximum, by 2040. Long before then, if they are right, the society that we suppose to be stable will start to crumble.

Already, in this last decade of the twentieth century, civilised standards are faltering. Dark Ages scenarios of senseless tribal, ethnic and religious savagery are no longer confined to the Third World, and up-to-date equivalents of the black death are baffling the doctors.

With the national and international outlook so bleak, the comfortable 'business as usual' assumption that has led to the conclusion that demand for Mendip limestone will grow steadily for the next 20 years is untenable. My prediction is that the next 20 years will see at most a modest increase, or quite possibly a decrease, in the national demand for aggregate.

THE SEARCH FOR ALTERNATIVES TO LIMESTONE

Glensanda Quarry, hidden among and dwarfed by the Strontian granite mountains beside Loch Linnhe, is the prototype for future mammoth coastal quarries able to ship aggregate in bulk carriers, 100,000 tonnes at a time, to the markets of South East England and elsewhere. Sea transport is stated to be 1/200th of the cost, per tonne-mile, of transport by road.

Other countries with huge coastal deposits of hard rock may now wish to ship aggregates to the markets. The basalt lavas of Iceland are particularly desirable because they are, like wood, a renewable resource. One eruption from the Laki volcano, in 1783-84, produced 12 cubic kilometres of basalt, enough to meet Britain's present demand for aggregate for 100 years. Basalt aggregate from Iceland should be cheap to produce because the quarrying is carried out naturally by the grinding action of glaciers, the waste material is washed away to sea in meltwater rivers, and the cleaned and graded basalt shingle accumulates as vast coastal plains like Chesil Beach magnified hundreds of thousands of times, ready to be dredged up and loaded into bulk carriers (Plate 6).

Coastal superquarries in gritstone and a variety of hard igneous rocks are now proposed from Norway through Scotland and Ireland to Spain. Before long they will be able to provide copious supplies of aggregate to reduce the pressure on environmentally friendly rocks such as the hard limestone of the Mendip Hills.

CONCLUSIONS

Predictions of an ever-increasing demand for construction aggregate are unreliable. Coastal superquarries in granite, gritstone and basalt will in due course be able to provide seaborne aggregate sufficient for the requirements of South East England. Hard limestone in situ is shown to be more valuable, economically and socially, and in both the short term and the long term, than hard limestone converted to aggregate. The time is ripe, therefore, to plan for a run-down of limestone quarries throughout Britain.

Planning authorities now have sound economic and environmental reasons to resist the extension of existing hard limestone quarries, or the opening of new ones, in the Mendips and in other limestone regions like the Peak District, the Yorkshire Dales and the karst landscapes of North and South Wales. However, the cheapness that puts hard limestone at improper risk is a serious obstacle that needs to be offset by an environmental levy or tax to bring it into the same cost range as other aggregates and to encourage recycling.

We have no right to deny to future generations all those pleasures, advantages and employment opportunities that we, the fortunate ones, derive from our limestone hills.

ACKNOWLEDGEMENTS

I am grateful to *Mineral Planning* and *New Scientist* magazines for permission to reprint parts of earlier articles. Dave Irwin, Tony Waltham and Kevin Wills gave invaluable help with the illustrations. Barney Butter, Hugh Cornwell, Alan Dawe, Richard Galsworthy, Paul Hodge, Barry Macrae, Richard Moon and John Pearce kindly commented on sections of the manuscript that impinged on their expertise; if I didn't invariably accept their advice the responsibility is mine.

REFERENCES

Barrington, N. and Stanton, W. 1977. *Mendip, the Complete Caves and a View of the Hills*. Cheddar Valley Press.

Department Of The Environment 1993. *Guidelines for Aggregates Provision in England and Wales* - Revision of MPG 6. Draft consultation document. DoE.

Harrisson, D. J., Buckley, D. K. and Marks, R. J. 1992. 'Limestone resources and hydrogeology of the Mendip Hills.' *British Geological Survey Technical Report* SA/92/19.

Hendy, P. 1981. 'Notes on the Netherworld.' *Journal of the Wessex Cave Club*, 16, 129-131.

Kellaway, G. A. (Ed) 1991. *The Hot Springs of Bath*. Bath City Council.

Pollock, D. 1989. 'Limestone from Somerset.' *Mineral Planning* (40), 3-7.

Stanton, W. I. 1966. 'The Impact of Limestone Quarrying on the Mendip Hills.' *Proceedings of the University of Bristol Speleological Society* 11, 54- 62.

———————— 1981. 'Further field evidence of the age and origin of the lead-zinc-silica mineralization of the Mendip region.' *Proceedings of the Bristol Naturalists Society* 41, 25-34.

MINERALS PLANNING POLICY

Richard Moon,
Assistant Director (Environmental Regulation),
Environment Department, Somerset County Council

Two key questions must be addressed:-
(1) what is the nature of the procedural and policy framework in which minerals planning takes place? and
(2) does this mechanism work successfully ?

It is important to recognise that local authorities do not operate in a vacuum, or with a free hand. They operate within a legal and policy framework which is set by national government and operated through Acts of Parliament, Statutory Instruments, Circular advice, Planning Policy Guidance Notes (PPGs), and, in the case of minerals, Mineral Planning Policy Guidance Notes (MPGs). Local authorities must work within this framework. Statute is also backed up by case law and together they provide the framework within which local authorities operate.

Individuals and businesses, as consumers of the planning service, look to the system for different results. Businesses find the planning service useful in enabling them to plan their operations; people look to it to enable them to take decisions that affect their own lives, and as it affects their immediate environment. However the rules do not allow for absolute certainty. Development plans are only the framework for decision making, they do not determine the decisions. Yet they are useless if they do not give some degree of certainty as to what is likely to happen in the future. What is not fully understood, or indeed accepted by some people, is that decisions which appear to be against the provisions of a plan (or some aspects of it) are often justified on the basis of the particular merits of a proposal, or because of other material considerations. However it must be acknowledged that current government policy is towards a 'plan-led' system. For this to be effective plans must be reviewed regularly ; if this is not done then decisions not in accordance with the plan could be justified on the basis that too much time has elapsed and that circumstances have changed.

The minerals planning system thus has a number of components :-

(1) The requirement in the Town and Country Planning Act 1990 for each county council to prepare a Structure Plan for its area which includes a strategic minerals policy.

(2) The Planning and Compensation Act 1991 which requires county councils to prepare Mineral Local Plans for the whole of their areas. There is a requirement for these plans to be in place, countrywide, by 1997.

(3) The arrangements for counties, through the Regional Planning Conference, to produce Regional Planning Advice, and for the Secretary of State to produce Regional Planning Guidance (RPG).

(4) Regional Aggregates Working Parties (RAWPs) provide a factual analysis of the minerals planning situation for Regional Planning Guidance. They also inform the Secretary of State so that he can produce the appropriate national advice for minerals planning, in particular in MPG6.

(5) Development control decisions on planning applications are submitted to the minerals planning authorities of county councils and metropolitan borough councils.

The task of the planner is to prepare advice for politicians, based on the above considerations, which they can accept, modify or reject. In preparing this advice they must consult, listen and balance the arguments. The essence of planning judgement lies in determining the balance of advantage between the need for development and the amount of environmental damage it may cause.

The theory behind the development plan system is sometimes referred to as the 'cascade principle', with increasing detail the more local the planning level. Thus at the national level PPGs and MPGs, backed up by ministerial statements, provide the current government policy for minerals planning authorities. At the regional level Regional Planning Guidance provides the broad strategic guidance for the region; again though, this is issued by the Secretary of State (and not, as some think, by regional elected government — which we do not have in the UK), or by the Regional Planning Conference (the grouping of locally-elected members of the region's local authorities).

At the county level the Structure Plan is based on this Regional Planning Guidance. The real detail is in the Minerals Local Plan, which includes specific policies and criteria at the level of local detail of OS-based proposals; but PPG1 (General Policy Principles) still requires that these proposals must be consistent with national and regional policy. The Secretary of State is a statutory consultee in the preparation of Development Plans. His powers of intervention allow him to direct a local planning authority to modify a draft plan, or indeed to call in a plan, or part of it, for his own determination.

Mineral Policy Guidance at the national level is set out in two documents, MPG1 (General Considerations and the Development Plan System) and MPG6 (Guidelines for Aggregate Provision in England and Wales); the latter is the more relevant to the present debate.

The key phrase in MPG6 is that the system 'must ensure that the construction industry receives a steady and adequate supply of material ... so that it can meet the needs of the community and that economic growth is not hindered.'

This objective does not mean that all agregates must be land-won primary aggregates — indeed earlier guidance had recognised the contribution from secondary aggregates, dredged material, and imports as other ingredients in the overall 'cake'. Extending this metaphor, the chef, currently Robin Mabey, Chief Planner at the DoE, and key adviser to the government on this issue, can choose not only ingredients, but also the proportions of each in the 'mix' of aggregates (Figure 21).

However, whatever the guidelines say, the market will ensure that only enough aggregates are produced to meet demand; mineral companies will not produce aggregate if there is no market for it. The significant point about the guidelines is that they are based on predictions of long-term demand, and that MPAs are required to ensure, through their plans and policies, that this demand can be met. If demand is lower than predicted these plans and policies

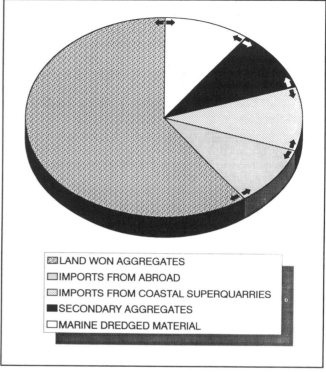

Figure 21 Options for the supply of aggregates.

LAND WON AGGREGATES
IMPORTS FROM ABROAD
IMPORTS FROM COASTAL SUPERQUARRIES
SECONDARY AGGREGATES
MARINE DREDGED MATERIAL

could thus lead to an over-commitment of land for mineral extraction, and an unnecessary extension of planning blight.

Over-provision in aggregate plans can thus have serious consequences. It can blight an area for a long time ahead; for, once land is allocated, it is very difficult for a minerals planning authority to reverse the position at a future plan stage. There is a further consequence in that, because land-won aggregates are in general closer to the market and cheaper to supply they will tend to be used in preference to other forms of aggregate; thus even though overall demand for aggregates may be lower than predicted, there is a risk that primary aggregates will continue to supply most of that demand, because the reduction in demand will fall

---

> ### TABLE 11
> #### OPTIONS FOR INTERFERENCE WITH PURE MARKET FORCES
>
> - Levies on primary land-won aggregates
>
> - Direct subsidy to help use of secondary aggregates
>
> - Revised specifications to assist use of secondary aggregates
>
> - Design of contracts requiring the use of secondary aggregates
>
> - Government intervention in re-shaping demand for facilities requiring use of aggregates (demand management) e.g. roads and other public works

mainly on secondary aggregates and imports. This emphasises the key importance of the demand forecasts, and their relationship to the final guideline figures.

In its latest draft guidelines the DoE has signalled a continuing increase in the national demand for aggregates, but with a shift in balance from land-won supply towards greater use of secondary aggregates and provision from coastal superquarries. However this does not signal a reduction in land-won supply; also, because of the long lead time in establishing alternative supply this is unlikely to have much impact in under 10 years. If these alternative sources of supply are to make a significant impact they must be encouraged (a) by moving slowly towards a restriction on traditional land-based allocations and permissions (with DoE and MPAs signalling that this will occur); (b) by fiscal measures which encourage private enterprise to use the best environmental option, including coastal quarries and superquarries and, if necessary, imports; and (c) by encouraging use of secondaries for appropriate defined end-uses — though probably not as direct substitutes for the best materials (Table 11).

The unknown factor in these projections is the actual demand for aggregates. Some have described current forecasts as broadly realistic because more aggregates will be used as the economy grows; others have criticised them as over-estimates. The problem is that if actual demand proves to be lower than the guidelines there will be little incentive for companies to vary their traditional policy by investing in coastal quarries and/or superquarries — the only realistic long-term alternative to locally based supplies.

A key feature of MPG6 (and of its revision) is the Regional Guidelines — policy statements which guide MPAs as to the anticipated demand in the period ahead for aggregates from their region. They indicate the amount of aggregates which will be needed from different sources to meet the demand scenario. This is broken down into 5-year blocks over the 20-year planning period, and through these it is possible to visualise a change in strategy; however managing such change has been likened to steering a supertanker.

Another feature of MPG6 is the landbank, which can be described as a stock of planning permissions for an area for the winning and working of minerals. It is a requirement in minerals planning for MPAs to maintain a landbank sufficient to enable the industry to respond to an increase in demand, taking account of the lead time needed to obtain planning permission and to bring a site into production. The current version of MPG6 requires a 10-year landbank, based on the average of the last 3 years' production, but the latest draft proposes to reduce this to 5 years so as to give MPAs more sensitive control — though for hard rock a longer, though unspecified, period is indicated. It is around this concept of the landbank that much of the argument is taking place because it is the only control on a secure supply and the only means of bringing it about.

How, then, do the Regional Aggregates Working Parties (RAWPs) work? They were set up in the early 1970s, and each has representatives from the MPAs, the industry and DoE, and from organisations such as British Rail, MAFF and the NRA. One of their roles is to collect and collate regional aggregates data from surveys carried out every 4 years. This data, provided by the companies and collated by each county in a standard format, includes reserves, total production, means of transport, end-use imports and destinations for export. Every 4 years, therefore, the government is provided with a detailed national picture of the aggregates industry from which trends can be identified.

The MPAs bring to the RAWP an overview of the environmental issues in their area and report on policy developments; the industry brings practical arguments about the market and production capabilities; the DoE representatives help to steer progress, knowing, as they do, what is happening in other regions.

The work of the individual regions is brought together through yet another body, the National Coordinating Group (NCG), whose meetings are attended by the chairmen of the RAWPs, and representatives of the industry (mainly BACMI and SAGA) and of DoE and other appropriate government departments. It provides a useful forum for discussion of policy developments and progress, and to inform the participants about the programmes and policies of government. The NCG is supported by a Technical Sub-Group which provides advice on specific issues.

The work of the individual RAWP, as far as the MPAs are concerned, is carried out by officers. Its work is non-political, which can make the officers' job difficult - perhaps more difficult than that of the industry representatives who can speak with more certainty. However the job is not impossible because the focus of the work is essentially an assembly of facts, a technical assessment of the future demand for aggregates in the region, and advice on the options for meeting that demand. This assessment involves taking a view on potential production in the region, on the demand from the region itself and from other regions, and on the likely contribution from waste and recycled materials, from marine-dredged aggregates, and from imports.

The work of each RAWP is reported in the 'Regional Commentary', the latest from the South West being dated January 1992. This report is widely circulated, and public reaction to it is made known to the MPAs, and through them to the Regional Planning Conference so that it can inform the Regional Planning Strategy. Consideration of the Commentaries from these bodies gives the DoE a 'political' view of regional aggregates policy. The Department then uses these Regional Commentaries in the preparation of national policy, in particular MPG6. Once MPG6 is published each RAWP must then prepare a county breakdown from the regional supply component.

It is generally accepted that the RAWPs perform a useful function and should be retained with broadly their present format. Because the officers on the RAWP are officials, and not politicians, it is sometimes difficult to reach a concensus view at the political or tactical level; but this problem is recognised by the other participants. Yet it is difficult to envisage how well-informed national and regional guidance could be provided without this forum; in practice any body whose main purpose is to collect data, research facts, assess broad environmental constraints and opportunities, and help different interests to share opinion and experience must be worthwhile.

Finally a comment on the different scales of operation, and on the current focus of interest on sustainability. At the global level the arguments about sustainability and about conserving the earth's natural resources for future generations are clearly made and well understood. At the national level the UK government has to translate these international objectives into national policy, conditioned as they are by European or continental objectives. The current exercise on the updating of MPG6, and future minerals strategy, taking account of sustainability, is the responsibility of government. This requires national strategic thinking, with the government and its advisers being informed by the Regional Commentaries, by the results of their own research and of visits to all parts of the country, and by the comments of interested parties. At the regional level the MPG6 guidelines will present clear advice as to the amounts of aggregates required; this advice will be based on facts, including current and future sources of supply, as well as judgements on 'sustainability', but will not itself specify locations. This is left to the county level, where the choice is now not about how much? but about where from?. Within an overarching strategic framework it is extremely difficult for a county to argue that it should produce less; in fact this would need a very convincing environmental argument — and paradoxically it is only through the Minerals Local Plan that such a case could be assembled.

There are thus a number of rules governing minerals planning that everyone interested in the debate should understand:-

(1) Government policy as set out in MPG1 and MPG6 provides the ground rules on which the exercise is based. It is not possible to deviate far from these, because at the end

of the day the Secretary of State has powers over both Structure Plans and Minerals Local Plans, and can appeal or 'call in' individual planning applications.

(2) Neither a region nor an individual minerals planning authority can act unilaterally in making a major policy shift. Change requires an argument to be well demonstrated and argued at the regional level; it needs to be defined and proven.

(3) The discretion that minerals planning authorities enjoy on their policy options can only be exercised after proper obligations have been fulfilled in terms of their consequences for other counties and regions.

(4) The minerals planning system represents a carefully constructed 'deck of cards' between MPAs, regions, government and industry. The scope for changing course in one area without creating problems in other areas is limited, at least in the short term; if change is to be made it must be through negotiation and agreement, and over the medium to long term.

It follows, therefore, that the current work being carried out on the Minerals Local Plan for Somerset will inform the Structure Plan, and so allow a thorough assessment of the constraints and of the sustainable contribution that Somerset can make to national aggregates supply. This in turn will inform the Regional Aggregates Working Parties in their inter-regional discussions about longer term balance of supply.

QUARRYING: THE ECONOMIC CASE

David Tidmarsh,
Foster Yeoman Quarries Ltd, Frome, Somerset

AGGREGATES - WHAT ARE THEY ?

Aggregates are bulk minerals which meet various technical requirements, such as volume, size, shape, hardness and chemical properties, primarily for use in the construction industry. Primary aggregates consist predominantly of crushed rock, or sand and gravel. Secondary aggregates include mineral and demolition wastes such as china clay waste and crushed concrete.

Aggregates are as much a part of modern living as are food and drink, not because they are a topical media issue, but because modern people demand the things of which aggregates are an essential, but passive, ingredient. Houses to live in, offices and factories to work in, schools and colleges to be educated in, hospitals to be healed in, shopping centres to shop in, roads to drive on, airports and seaports to travel from, railways to commute and travel on, sewerage works to treat our wastes, water treatment plants to purify water — even down to the mundane items of life such as paints, glass and toothpaste. These all make up the demand and supply equation for aggregates in a modern civilised society.

As can be seen from Figure 22, there has been a long-established trend for aggregate demand to increase at about 3.7% per annum, from about 80M tonnes in 1955 to a peak demand of 300M tonnes in 1989. More interestingly, but perhaps not surprising, the Figure also shows the close relationship that there has been between demand for aggregates and Gross Domestic Product, of which construction output is a key indicator. To my mind GDP can also broadly be called economic growth; as such, when we have a growing economy we all have that 'feel-good' feeling — yet we conveniently tend to forget the resulting impact on demand for aggregates.

Before we enter the debate on which aggregates, and from where, let us not forget that we, as individuals, create the

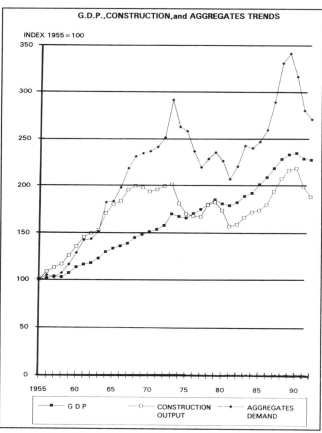

Figure 22 Changes in GB aggregates demand, Gross Domestic Product and construction output, 1955-1992.

TABLE 12
ANNUAL AGGREGATES USE PER HEAD OF POPULATION (TONNES)

Italy	5.0
UK	5.2
Germany	6.7
France	6.8
USA	6.8
Japan	10.0

generally want to improve the quality of their lives; stagnant economies eventually die.

This is not a scenario peculiar to the UK. Our European partners also have similar demand/supply problems, and by general European standards our demand per head of population is rather low (Table 12).

THE SECTORAL DEMAND FOR AGGREGATES

As can be seen from Figure 23, the broad sectors af aggregate demand in the UK have changed, particularly over the last 15 years, from being predominantly taxpayer-funded to a more even balance between the taxpayer and the private sector. I suspect that this shift is unlikely to be maintained, and that we are likely to move back towards the proportions of the early 1980s; in particular the

demand in one way or another so that we, as individuals, also have control over that demand. I suspect that, in reality, it is a control we are unlikely to exercise, for people

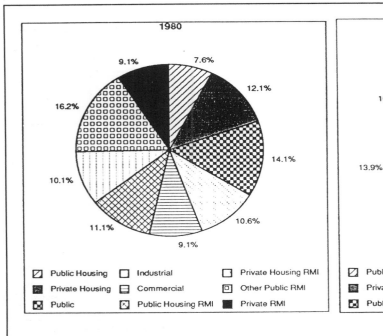
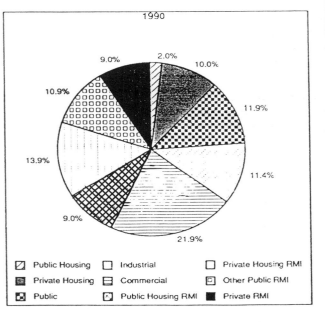

Figure 23 Composition of construction output, 1980 and 1990.

enormous growth in private funding in the commercial sector seems unlikely to be repeated.

The sector that currently draws most attention is the roads programme, but I believe that people are misguided to believe that a curtailment of road construction would actually reduce the demand for aggregates. Currently over 70% of the aggregates used for roads are consumed in road maintenance and minor road improvements. Furthermore, should the proposed road programme be curtailed, as some critics advise, yet traffic continue to increase at the rate forecast by the Department of Transport, the damage to existing roads resulting from the increased traffic would mean that maintenance and minor improvements would continue to use at least the current quantity of aggregates. The same applies to the railways which, with their existing infrastructure, are a significant user of aggregates in the form of rail ballast. More intensive use, whether for freight or passengers, would intensify the use of aggregates; it would also increase the demand on feeder services to the rail network, mainly by lorry, motor-car or bus, with consequent greater demands on the road infrastructure.

It is difficult to escape the fact that with a mobile population, whether it is travelling to work, meeting friends, going on holiday, or carrying goods, an efficient transport infrastructure is essential to modern life. Such an infrastructure must be built and maintained, and we cannot ignore that both construction and maintenance create a demand for aggregates.

SUPPLY AND DEMAND FOR AGGREGATES

As part of national minerals planning the government, since the end of the last war, has attempted to estimate the future demand for aggregates. A number of different economic models have been used but, almost without exception, these have under-forecast the actual demand. Fortunately the planning system has been sufficiently flexible and robust to respond to these unpredicted levels of demand.

Conscious of its failure to forecast accurately the long-term demand for aggregates the government has recently made strenuous efforts to improve its forecasting methods. In this it has used the skills of Cambridge Econometrics, who have a good record of forecasting both national and regional construction demands, and of ECOTEC, who have modelled the historical relationship between construction output and demand for aggregates, and who have developed what can only be described as the most researched assessment of future demand (Figure 24). It must be emphasised that the demand forecasts can only be an extrapolation of historical relationships between aggregate demand, GDP growth and construction output; if the economy grows and performs in its historical way then

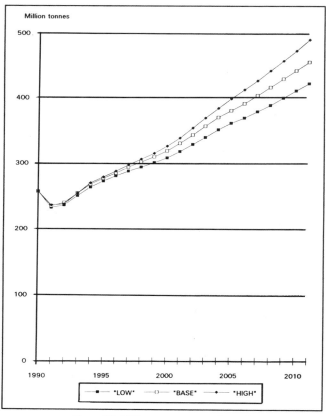

Figure 24 GB forecast aggregate demand trends; base', 'high' and 'low' projections.

the demand forecasts will materialise. But these forecasts are not objectives that must be met; they are guidelines against which planning decisions should be considered; and they are subject to regular review.

It is interesting to note that, although Figure 24 shows the impact of the recession over the past 4 years, the long-term impact of that recession is only a small reduction in the rate of increase in demand over the whole period. It is quite obvious that we are unlikely to have the utopia of continuous steady economic growth; there will be ups and downs within any period so that, as such, the forecast only reflects a trend. Thus had we discussed the forecast in 1989 I suspect that most of us would have considered it was achievable. Discussing it today, after 4 years of recession, we take a more pessimistic view. I wonder what our view will be in 4 years time? Yet it is that longer-term view

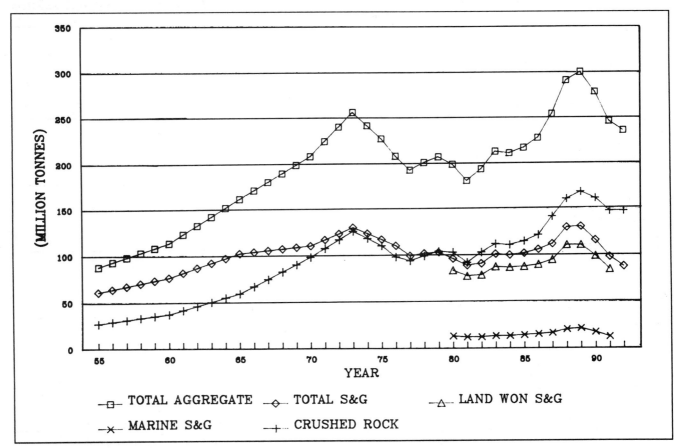

Figure 25 Changes in total aggregate production in England and Wales since 1955, and in composition of the aggregate used.

which is essential in planning for future aggregates demand.

SOURCES OF AGGREGATES

Aggregates have many different uses; they also come from many different sources. Figure 25 illustrates the changes in aggregate demand in England and Wales over the past few years, as well as trends in the pattern of supply. Most notable is the decline in the contribution of land-won sand

and gravel and the increase in the contribution from marine aggregates and crushed rock. The reasons for these changes are simple, though they may not be obvious. Marine aggregate supply is progressively replacing land-won sand and gravel, for which it has become increasingly difficult to get planning permission to extract. Demand for crushed rock has grown as technical specifications, mainly in respect of major roads, have progressively excluded the use of sand and gravel, notably in sub-base and macadams.

The government is currently reviewing its Mineral Planning Guidance for aggregates (MPG6). This is the

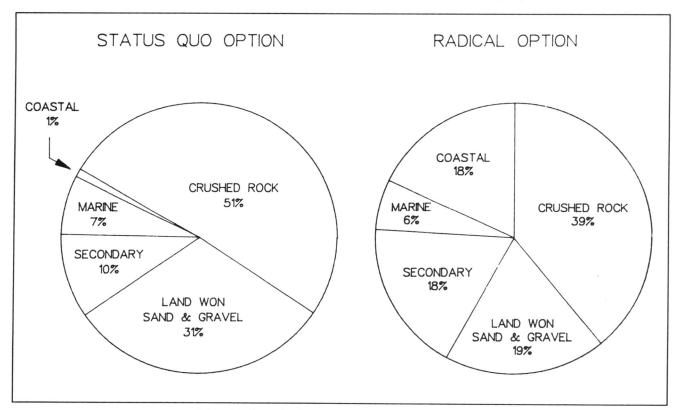

Figure 26 Alternative future aggregate supply options, year 2011.

statement of Government policy as to the criteria against which mineral applications should be determined, and the demand, if it materialises, should be satisfied. Clearly, over the last decade the environmental awareness of the whole population has risen and, quite properly, will continue to rise — an increased environmental awareness which, in my view, is a direct result of higher living standards; yet, as already explained, these higher standards perversely create an increased demand for aggregates. They also continue to create conflicts — for, let us be under no illusion, aggregates can only be won from where they are located.

In looking at how aggregate demand into the next century can best be satisfied the government has undertaken significant reviews, based on consultants' reports, of two supply options that currently contribute only a small proportion to present aggregates supply, namely use of secondary aggregates and increased supplies from coastal superquarries. Two possible scenarios were included in a consultative document on MPG6 issued early in 1993. (Figure 26). One of these, which I will call the status quo, is essentially a projection into the future of the existing supply pattern, with only a small increase coming from greater use of secondary aggregates and coastal superquarries, and with the balance coming from land-won sand and gravel, marine aggregates and crushed rock. The second, and more radical, option, would require an increasing proportion of total supply to come from secondary aggregates and coastal superquarries. But let there be no doubt; wherever the aggregates come from there will be environmental impact. Surely what the government must be striving for is the best possible balance between these options.

WHY THE MENDIPS ?

Construction aggregates in the past were always quarried at the closest point of use; drive up any Roman road and every mile or so you will find, immediately adjacent to the road, a small quarry from which the road material was won. However this 'borrow pit' approach became progressively less practical, and resources further from the point of use must now be utilised. This has, of course, increased the cost of the product because of the higher cost of transport, and transport costs have now become a significant factor in modern aggregate supply.

For all practical purposes there are no reserves of hard rock south of a line drawn from the Wash to Bournemouth; the nearest sources of rock to the South East of England are the limestones of the Mendip Hills and the granites surrounding Leicester.

Historically the large limestone reserves in the Mendips had better road and rail connections to most parts of the South East than the granites in Leicestershire. These are in smaller deposits, and with poor transport links, so that the products, which are mainly used in skid-resistant road surfaces and rail ballast, are significantly more expensive.

After the war the Mendip quarries, originally developed to supply the local markets, were expanded to supply a larger roadborne market going down into Wiltshire and Hampshire. By the early 1970s the quarries had been further developed to supply, principally by rail, across the whole of the South East. Currently some 60% of Mendip production is consumed within the South West, with the remaining 40% exported to the South East.

In 1972 Somerset County Council, which for its time was a very forward thinking authority, produced a minerals plan which aimed to concentrate quarrying activity on the East Mendips, preserving the West Mendips, already designated as an Area of Outstanding Natural Beauty, for the more limited quarrying of higher quality limestone for use in the steel industry. That plan, which is still substantially the mineral plan of the local authority, has reduced the number of operating units in Somerset from something over 30 to just 9 operations, of which 6 are in the East Mendips. Two of these, Whatley and Torr Works, can be considered as superquarries, with a significant proportion of their output being transported by rail to the South East.

The Mendips embrace a land area of approximately 26 sq. miles, of which only 2,500 acres (1,000 hectares) has permission to be worked for minerals. The total quantity of minerals with planning permission is estimated to be about 550M tonnes, which at the 1989 rate of extraction of 20M tonnes would last through to 2020. However not all these reserves are at currently active quarry sites.

As with any mineral extraction there are inevitably sources of environmental conflict, with the principal impacts being from road transportation, noise, dust, blasting and hydrogeological damage. The industry has taken significant steps to minimise all these impacts over the last 10-15 years, and is committed to further improvements for the future.

Modern planning permissions limit noise levels at quarry boundaries, and regular monitoring ensures that these levels are seldom exceeded. All quarry operations also have to be authorised under the Environmental Protection Act, and discharges such as dust and wastes, including oils and run-off water, are all controlled. The industry has actively cooperated in routing vehicles so as to avoid the most sensitive environmental areas, and in many cases has made direct and indirect contributions to road improvements. All quarrying in the Mendips is operated in accordance with the BACMI Environmental Code; this not only sets environmental standards but is also an environmental management system to ensure that such standards are reviewed and maintained.

The hydrology of the Mendips, as Peter Smart has described, is highly complex. Thus quarry companies have spent considerable sums on studies by hydrogeological consultants in order to gain a better understanding of the hydrogeology as it affects each quarry, and have engineered schemes to relieve any problems that might arise. The National Rivers Authority and the County Council have had a policy where sub-water table working is required on a bench by bench approach. This gives the local authority and the NRA some control should the consultants' forecasts prove incorrect — even though in some quarrying circumstances this can cause considerable operational problems for the operator.

Water and limestone are both natural resources which we, as individuals, wish to use; wherever possible, a balance has to be struck between the two. Unfortunately we have had, and continue to have, a situation in which the water resource is treated as sacrosanct, with the mineral resource taking second place. I believe that, provided adequate measures are taken to protect the demand on the water resources then it is desirable, within the overall balance, that the limestone resource should also be allowed to be developed.

The aftercare potential of quarries should also not be underestimated. Quarrying below the water table greatly increases the water-storage capacity, from about 1% in the natural rock to 100% in the water-filled quarry, with the

water available for supply purposes. Furthermore worked-out quarries can become valuable sites for wildlife by recreating limestone habitats now lost to agriculture and forestry. There are opportunities both for continued industrial use and for recreational use; far from destroying valued countryside quarries can actively increase the potential uses of the countryside, as part of the continuing process of change by which human activity has shaped almost all of the UK countryside.

Within the 26 sq. miles of the Mendips the common perception is that the whole of the area from Frome to Cheddar is a continuous reserve of limestone suitable for quarrying. This is absolutely incorrect — as Ramous Gallois has made clear. It is probable that, given no environmental constraints, less than 10% of the Mendips contains suitable limestone that could possibly be worked; the concept of the Mendips being 'flattened' is both emotional and geologically unrealistic.

Quarrying of limestone in the Mendips is of course a major business, and of considerable importance in the local economy. I estimate that in 1989 the total turnover of construction material based on limestone was in excess of £150 M. In addition to 20M tonnes of limestone more than a million tonnes of coated material (tarmac or asphalt) are produced from Mendip-based plants, together with a significant number of precast products, including blocks, slabs, kerbs and pipes which are produced in local factories. The total turnover of course includes haulage, itself a major business attached to the quarrying industry.

In 1989 more than 1,000 people were employed directly in quarrying in the Mendips, while probably a further 2,000 were employed in transportation and manufacturing concrete products. In a predominantly rural area employment on this scale is highly important, with alternative employment virtually impossible to find with the decline in agriculture and the fall-off in work in the defence industries located round the fringes of the Mendips.

As well as employment, much of the social and economic structure of the villages and hamlets of the Mendip Hills currently depends on the quarrying industry. In comparison the water industry generates approximately £50M annually from its Mendip resources, and employs relatively few people, either directly or indirectly; as such it contributes little to either the social or the economic life of the Mendips.

OTHER SOURCES OF SUPPLY OF AGGREGATES

There is a common belief that a decline in the contribution of sand and gravel to total aggregate supply has been made up by increased quarrying of crushed rock. This is simply not true. Even today less than 3% of the Mendip limestone that is transported to the South East is used in concrete, which has traditionally used sand and gravel. The increase in the demand for crushed rock is the result almost exclusively of the higher specification now set for road construction and reconstruction — itself a direct result of the increase in pavement thickness from about 380 mm in the 1970s to 970 mm today, as lorry axle weights have increased.

Sand and gravel are normally rounded in shape, and have a low frictional resistance when under compression, whereas the angular crushed rock has a significantly higher frictional resistance under similar compression (axle loading), and gives better strength and longer performance. This angularity also creates a denser material, reducing the amount of water absorbed and thus reducing the amount of damage by frost.

There is a large, though finite, reserve of aggregate under the seabed, broadly around the coast from the Wash to Southampton. This reserve of marine sand and gravel has been developed since the early 1950s, and output is likely to increase to something around 30-35M tonnes per annum. Unfortunately most of the deposits are associated with fishing grounds and fish breeding areas, and so have significant conflict with both fishing and fish stock conservation, so that any further increase in output is most unlikely. Suitable reserves are almost totally confined to the coast adjacent to Southern England, as materials found off the Dutch, Belgian and French coasts contain very little of the coarser fractions essential for concrete.

The Arup report, 'Occurrence of Waste Products', reviewed in detail all the locations and production of waste materials in the UK. There is absolutely no doubt that there are considerable reserves of waste products, most of which are regularly being added to. Unfortunately the vast majority of these wastes do not have the technical qualities necessary for them to replace a significant part of current aggregate production. For example the winning of china clay generates considerable quantities of waste. However this waste is predominantly a very coarse sand, which, although it has been used in some concretes requires excessive amounts of cement because of its physical properties which cannot be changed. It also produces a concrete on which it is virtually impossible to produce a surface finish that is aesthetically acceptable, and which is also vulnerable to atmospheric attack.

The winning and transport of waste materials also causes very much the same environmental problems as occur with virgin materials. Thus china clay wastes are mainly situated in Cornwall, which has poor road, rail and sea infrastructure; even if the material were more technically suitable I believe, on balance, that the environmental disadvantages of using it would be significantly greater than the winning of virgin aggregates in most current locations.

There has also, in recent years, been an increased use of construction waste materials; virtually all old asphalt (road planings) is now reused in one form or another and recent changes in specification, which allow up to 10% to be used in new asphalt manufacture, will significantly increase its use in original value production.

People's attention will probably also have been drawn to the increased use of small mobile crushers on construction and demolition sites, allowing reuse of crushed material. However, although in Germany and the Netherlands sub-base material must, by regulation, contain 25% of waste material, it is noticeable that the thickness of sub-base in those countries is significantly greater than in the UK. As a result the use of new aggregates, per km of road, is very similar to that in the UK — and not, as might be expected, 25% less.

The most recent new contributors to aggregate supply have been the coastal superquarries, from which the product is transported by oceangoing vessels — a concept initiated by Sir Ralph Verney in the 1976 report 'Aggregates — The Way Ahead'. The first of these quarries, at Glensanda in Western Scotland, was started in 1986 and has currently lifted its output to just over 5M tonnes per annum. Within the revised MPG6 the government is proposing a significantly increased production from these sources. Most coastal superquarries will be in remote locations, in Scotland or perhaps in Norway; however this new source of aggregates requires facilities for oceangoing ships to land their cargoes. Such facilities, particularly in the South East, are limited; furthermore a sea-terminal handling perhaps 3 to 4M tonnes of aggregates annually must be at a location contiguous with a major road and, preferably, railway.

CONCLUSION

One cannot deny the inextricable link between aggregate demand and GDP. It is also unreasonable to expect this link to be changed without a fundamental rethink of the way in which we, the population, wish to build our lives. For the demand for aggregates is not created by the aggregates industry, or indeed, by the construction industry; it is created by the demands of society.

It is also useful to put this in perspective. Within overall aggregate supply less than 0.3% of the surface area of the UK is being used for aggregate extraction; moreover a more efficient use of primary aggregates has started so as to ensure that the best materials are used only for the highest specification purposes, with greater use of secondary aggregates for lower specifications. Of course this change in emphasis will not happen overnight; but the change is underway, and I am sure we shall see a better balance between the different supply options as the next century approaches.

Within this balance the Mendip Hills will continue to play an important role. For it is unrealistic to demand that extraction of limestone from the Mendips, or indeed from any other major source, should cease - if only because this would put additional pressure on the remaining sources that go to make the total supply of aggregates demanded by the people.

Data for all the Figures, except Figure 23, are from BACMI, the British Aggregate Construction Material Industries. Figure 23 is from S. G. Warburg Securities.

QUARRYING IN MENDIP: PLANNING PERSPECTIVES

Humphrey Temperley,
Chairman, Environment Committee, Somerset County Council

My colleague, Richard Moon, has described the way in which minerals extraction is planned in England and Wales. Much of this planning is strategic; in my view the real problems arise in preparing the Minerals Local Plan, which has to translate broad strategy into detailed proposals for action over the next 20 years. There are no easy answers.

Minerals have been extracted from the Mendips for many years, and history suggests that we can 'live with' an output around the 1985 level of 15M tonnes without too many problems. With identified reserves in Somerset of about 600M tonnes, at that level of output we could meet demand for some 40 years. That is a reasonable timescale to deal with an issue of this complexity, and we could write up a Minerals Plan to deal with it.

The problem is that the latest draft of the key planning document, MPG6, would require Somerset to provide up to 32M tonnes of aggregate per year; as one of our Mineral Officers put it, rather succinctly, 'at this stage it would be difficult to meet this long-term forecast demand in a manner consistent with sustainable development.' As a politician I agree with this comment, and find it difficult to envisage meeting the 32M tonnes forecast in an acceptable way. We are hoping that the delay in issuing the final version of MPG6 indicates a rethink, and that the forecasts are being revised downwards. However it is difficult to see how this can happen with the methodology used — a long and iterative statistical process, based on a fairly mindless extrapolation of existing trends.

I do not propose to go into detail as to whether our output could be 12M or 15M tonnes a year, but to look at some of the guiding principles. Firstly, mineral workings are concentrated in the East Mendips, and there are large areas of the Mendips with no workings. Our first task is to get the constraints on mineral working mapped and understood. There are three strategic constraints — water resources, Areas of Outstanding Natural Beauty and Sites of Special Scientific Interest, some of which, in my view, should be inviolable. The water constraint, as Peter Smart has shown, is important, for much of the limestone resource of East Mendip is the source of water for the Frome area — a serious issue for us to deal with, particularly in the area of Whatley and Halcombe. I assume that quarrying will not be allowed in the AONB, which means that some difficult choices will have to be made.

The examples of the quarries at Batts Combe, Whatley, Torr Works and Halcombe illustrate some of the problems. Batts Combe has created a wide and visible scar on the horizon, and with appalling access for lorries; Halcombe shows how close a quarry can be to a village; at Whatley the accelerating rate of extraction is rapidly changing the whole landscape; Torr illustrates the size and depth of the holes that can be left behind.

Thus with these constraints I do not believe that we should even attempt to accommodate a forecast at the 32M tonnes level; I believe my colleagues in other county councils in the South West will be saying very much the same.

But if not from the South West, where from? Willie Stanton has suggested increased output from coastal superquarries, or imports from abroad. But I have to tell you that people in Scotland are not over the moon over this proposal; Scottish National Heritage have serious concerns about a possible 5 to 10 new superquarries on their coast, and their chairman, Magnus Magnusson, also has views about exports from his native Iceland (Plate 6). We hope to invite him down to the South West next spring to open up a wider national debate.

Certainly, though, we must look at alternatives. Thus a large area near St Austell is littered with vast quantities of china clay sand and stent waste, rather like a scene from hell. Much of this would be available to the market if we could provide the necessary transport infrastructure. In other areas there are huge piles of minestone and slate waste, and other secondary and tertiary materials. Again these would need improved transport links — and in many cases rewriting of construction specifications so as to encourage their use. One mechanism we have suggested in Somerset is a small levy on primary aggregates so as to encourage the marketing of secondary aggregates — a 20-30p levy per tonne would be very useful. As a council we are also doing what we can to encourage the use of these materials in road contracts — not an easy option. One recent proposal was opposed by three parish councils; it was eventually permitted and is now seen as an acceptable, and environmentally sensible, long-term solution.

I believe this element could make a valuable contribution, both locally and nationally — though I am sure that government would argue that they have already taken account of increased use of secondary aggregates in their planning.

However where I do take issue with them is with the assumption that future economic growth will be at the same rate as in the last 20 years. I am sure many of us are clear that growth at that rate is unlikely, and should certainly not be regarded as sustainable development. If we are to have an aceptable standard of living we must do something to prevent 'the whole of the South East' being covered in concrete. We must find other ways of earning a living — as I said recently to a SE audience, 'visit the Mendips before they visit you.'

But let us suppose the worst scenario — that we are told we must meet the government demand in full. Where do we go? Do we allow quarrying in the AONB, in Asham Wood, or in the area east of Mells Park? I believe that the Mendip plateau, the water resources and the SSSI are too important to be released. Thus in my view it is almost impossible to find 'acceptable' new areas for quarrying.

So do we defy Government and say 'it can't be done'? — and risk ad hoc applications and approvals because we have not met regional planning guidance. We could, of course, fudge the issue by adopting the post-NIMBY strategy of NIMTO — 'not in my term of office' — and reducing the timescale of the plan, allocating the minimum, and leaving the problem to the future. I am sure that that is not the answer, and that we must use the next few years constructively; we need to persuade government to reduce the forecast demand figures significantly, and to encourage recycling and use of secondary aggregates. We also have a big educational task ahead of us in persuading the public that we cannot base our future economy on the unrestrained use of a limited resource, and that we must plan for lower levels of output, using limestone only for the uses for which it is essential.

To conclude, therefore, I believe that there can be an agreed, and stable, future for quarrying in Somerset, and for the people of Somerset, at an output something near the present 15M tonnes level. At the same time the industry will need to diversify and add value to its products, and to operate to the very best environmental standards. At that rate the industry could have a life of 30 to 40 years; after that I believe it must decline and eventually disappear. Long before then I hope we shall have discovered a better way of providing for our needs than digging up the Mendip Hills.

A view of Batts Combe Quarry, emphasising the proximity of human habitation. (Courtesy of The Mid Somerset Series).

An interior view of the workings at Batts Combe Quarry. (Courtesy of the Mid Somerset Series).

Industrial Mendip. Old water-wheel at Wadbury ironworks. (Courtesy of Eunice Overend).

THE CHANGING ECOLOGY OF MENDIP

Eunice Overend,
Chippenham, Wiltshire

Twelve thousand years ago, at the end of the last ice age, Mendip was a craggy world of snow in winter, but with the spring thaw much faster than in the more northerly tundras of today. This sent mud slides down the slopes, with torrents of meltwater gouging out valleys in the frozen ground — westward through Cheddar Gorge and eastward to where the Mells River cuts a mini-gorge in Vallis Vale. As the ground greened and insects multiplied, wildfowl and waders arrived to take advantage of the bountiful summer, flying south again with their young as the snows returned.

During this period of warming, each year more seedlings were able to survive a little further north, where previously the frost had killed them; at the same time birds had to fly further to find the right nesting place. From the south other plants, which had previously found Mendip too chilly, spread up the slopes, and the animals that ate them followed. With no Channel in between, the same was happening all the way to the Continent so that, within a thousand years, trees began to reach all but the most inhospitable places. Among the flowering herbs, grasses and sedges of the tundra — crowberry (*Empetrum nigrum*), dwarf birch (*Betula nana*), willow (*Salix spp*) — had a place. Juniper (*Juniperis communis*) followed; descendants of these plants, the last stand of juniper in Somerset, with its accompanying limestone flowers, were eradicated from a Laverton farm (ST 761535) around 1960, courtesy of a MAFF land improvement grant.

The first forests that developed were of birch and Scots pine. Birch is still present, but pine could not survive so far south, although it has been reintroduced. Aspen soon followed on the wetter ground. It propagates readily by suckers; thus some of the present stands could well be clones of, and so genetically identical with, the original trees.

These three species, together with willow, have light seeds which are windborne[1]. The first shrubs probably used 'internal' transport (as can be seen on the chalk downland of Salisbury Plain Training Area, taken over by the Army 50 years ago). The rough grassland is thickly sprinkled with developing scrub, all berry-bearing, of hawthorn, whitebeam, wayfaring tree, dogwood, spindle, dewberry, blackthorn and elder. Overflying fieldfares are the most probable carriers of seed of all but the last two. Blackthorn and elder mark badger paths. Hazel appears to colonise from old coppice at a speed governed by the distance woodmice carry nuts for storage; it rarely appears at new sites. Oak also needs a carrier; the most likely is the jay, poking acorns into the turf for winter feed. Oak prefers heavier land but ash, which arrived at about the same time, thrives on the thin limestone soils of the Mendips. Ash, spread by windborne keys, never seems to colonise far from the parent tree. The same is true for the native wych elm, whose pollen all but disappeared at a particular Neolithic level in the peat. This was once thought to be due to intensive felling as a result of an upsurge in agriculture, but is more likely to have resulted from an earlier epidemic of the same disease which our trees have suffered recently. Lime — small-leaved lime (*Tilia cordata*), not the planted hybrid variety — arrived later, about the same time as the beginning of agriculture, when warmer summers allowed viable seed to set. Like hazel it has always been coppiced, mainly for its bast — the long, strong fibres from under the bark which provided the only source of rope until hemp

[1] Canadian scientists have recently noticed the same thing happening as burnt sites are recolonised in both coniferous forest and tundra — birch and poplar seedlings are more common than conifers. They predict that global warming will allow deciduous trees, especially those with effective ways of dispersing seeds over long distances, to become more abundant and to invade the tundra a little further after each fire. Warmer and drier conditions could make wildfires more common, so accelerating the trend. (*New Scientist*, 29 January, 1994)

and coconut fibre began to be imported (and was still used in the bast mats of Victorian greenhouses). Coppiced lime sprouts round the outside, so that a stump becomes a stool which in turn becomes a ring which continues to grow as the poles are cut. Again stools on the ring become the centre of other circles; at the western end of Asham Wood (ST 703445) there is a pattern of such rings which, if mapped, would probably show that they are all clones of a single original tree — an interesting exercise for DNA testing.

The thinner soils on the steep slopes could not support trees but, as the ground warmed up, windborne seeds settled to produce a flower-rich turf, including thyme (*Thymus polytrichus*), rock-rose (*Helianthemum nummularium*), cowslip (*Primula veris*), salad burnet (*Sanguisorba minor*), milkwort (*Polygala vulgaris*), hawkweed (*Hieracium spp.*) and orchids (*Dactylorhiza spp.*). Such turf when grazed, which controls coarse grasses, may contain thirty or more different species per square metre, with nationally-scarce plants such as Cheddar pink (*Dianthus gratianopolitanus*) and Welsh poppy (*Meconopsis cambrica*) still present in the more inaccessible places.

Ash would have become the dominant tree on the plateau, as it still is, together with introduced sycamore, in hedgerows today. On the deeper soils above the sandstone, in the valleys, and at the eastern end where the limestone begins to run under the Jurassic rocks, oak would predominate. Woodland flowers, which need shade, followed the trees, although slowly. Some, which are now used as marker species for woods that have never been cleared for agriculture, may eventually recolonise suitable adjoining land, but they are unlikely ever to reach the isolated woodland areas, however large, now being replanted on farmland. Among these marker species are lily of the valley (*Convallaria majalis*), Solomon's seal (*Polygonatum multiflorum*), autumn crocus (*Colchicum autumnalis*), herb paris (*Paris quadrifolia*), woodruff (*Galium odoratum*), sanicle (*Sanicula europaea*), wood spurge (*Euphorbia amygdaloides*), and moschatel (*Adoxa moschatellina*), all now rare because so few woods remain.

The conservation value of grassland and woodland is assessed mainly by the number of plant species present. Plants are big enough to be seen — and many people recognise them; but there are few experts specialising in invertebrates, except perhaps in butterflies and moths. Holly blue butterflies need both holly and ivy together — not too difficult, but each plant species and assemblage has its own dependent insects, and produces its own microhabitat for unsuspected communities. Once destroyed this is can never be remade.

Most of the mammals that colonised the Mendips as soon as conditions were suitable still live there, but there were also wolves and bears, beavers and wild boar, and aurochs, the huge wild cattle that grazed in the open ash woods, together with red deer and, in the early days, reindeer and wild horses. But until man introduced them, no mink or grey squirrels, fallow deer or rabbits, or rats (water voles, not then confined to river banks, took their place).

For the next four thousand years these animals were hunted by the Mesolithic people, using stone-tipped arrows and spears. Little changed, except that first reindeer, and then horses, moved on as forest replaced the grassland. Arrowheads were mainly of flint, traded from the downlands to the east, but some were of chert found in bands in the limestone — the first use by man of Mendip stone. Man was in balance with his environment and virtually all the mammal species survived into historic times. The last known wild aurochs were on Mendip in the Bronze Age; polecats, pine martens and wild cats remained until the advent of pheasants, along with their attendant gamekeepers. Much the same happened with bird species, with birds of prey suffering the most acute persecution.

Neolithic agriculture brought with it forest clearance, slowly at first with pigs domesticated from wild boar and cattle from aurochs, increasing in pace as browsing goats and nibbling sheep were introduced from across the Channel. Seedcorn brought flowering weeds, including poppy (*Papaver spp.*), cornflower (*Centaurea cyanus*), charlock (*Sinapis arvensis*), and spurrey (*Spergula arvensis*), which modern sprays have scarcely mastered. Later much of the impoverished arable land reverted to rough grass and heather — as on Blackdown and Priddy North Hill. Until fields were enclosed in the nineteenth century most of Mendip was open, close-cropped sheepwalk, full of flowering herbs.

Iron ore is found in Mendip as red haematite that stains the rocks, and Iron Age man must have found and used it. The exact sites are not known because they have been covered by later workings, in use up to the time of Fussells of Mells' ironworks in the valley at Wadbury, which survived long enough to be photographed (Plate 6). Iron Age man, too, opened up the first tiny stone quarry (ST 676456) in the side of a valley at Downhead Common where quartz conglomerate for querns could be found. A beehive quern that matched this stone was uncovered when the overburden was removed for quarrying at Tedbury Iron Age fort (ST7448) during the last war.

Fussells' ironworks, in the gorge below Wells, specialised in high-grade edge-tools. At first they used local ore (later importing it from Sweden), and local coal (some converted to gas) and water power for the tilt-hammers. The resulting ash and slag was stacked up behind brick walls to widen the site for yet more building, leaving the river running in a canyon. Was this valley ruined? No: it is now a Site of Special Scientific Interest, with snowdrops (*Galanthus nivalis*), monkshood (*Aconitum napellus*), and alternate-leaved golden saxifrage (*Chrysosplenium alternifolium*), and is the only place in the country with patches of the big blue skullcap (*Scutellaria altissima*), which the Fussells themselves must have brought from the Mediterranean. Mosses, liverworts and ferns, including the brittle bladder fern (*Cystopteris fragilis*), fill the lighter parts of the wet tunnels below the works. The last Mendip otter had a holt here; and here too is a winter roost for both greater and lesser horseshoe bats. There was a breeding roost in the derelict manager's house until vandals burnt it down — fortunately at night when they were out.

How did the valley recover so quickly? The answer seems to lie in the shape of the site. Though a good half-mile long it is nowhere more than 100 metres wide, and with steep, rocky slopes towering above. This is within the range that woodland plants can colonise and, apart from a few small quarries to supply the limekilns, most of the slopes have never been touched. This persistence of the original vegetation in awkward places also accounts for the wood in Tedbury Camp above, which must have been cleared in Iron Age times, containing marker species such as autumn crocus and Solomon's seal.

The nearest coal to the ironworks lies just to the north of the limestone, between Vobster and Stratton Moor, continuing northward under the newer rocks beyond Radstock. In the south the seams, matching the limestone,

stand up on edge, and have been followed down since Roman times. Edford Wood, (ST 6648) near Holcombe, has these grooves with ditches leading to the river, together with a pond in the bell pit where coal was worked at a deeper level once pumping was invented. Abandoned now for more than a hundred years it, too, has recovered, although the site, perhaps 20 hectares, is much larger than that at Wadbury. It is full, in spring, of snowdrops, daffodils (*Narcissus pseudo-narcissus*), primroses (*Primula vulgaris*) and bluebells (*Hyacinthoides non-scripta*), and would pass at first glance as undisturbed woodland — if the badger-sett in a coal-tip did not betray what is underneath. The answer in this case seems to be the long-term but small-scale nature of the workings, so that there were always patches of undisturbed natural regeneration which allowed the original vegetation to hang on. An adjoining piece of newer woodland demonstrates how slowly most woodland species spread, even when conditions seem to be ideal.

The flowers that occur in such abundance are all species that set seed freely. If a few of these seeds reach a new place, perhaps on the wheels of a vehicle, and establish themselves they can in a short time spread far afield. Buddleia (*Buddleja davidii*) is the expert at this. A few chance seeds from the gardens of the 1950s, and large areas of bare limestone and quarry tips are now covered in the 'butterfly bush'.

One such site is the quarry at Tedbury Camp, served by a tramway which, pre-war, carried stone down the valley to Hapsford. Hapsford is the end of the Mells river 'gorge', where the limestone finally disappears eastwards underground.

Old limekilns in the valley show the original use for the stone, but Vallis Vale, where Nunney Brook meets the Mells river, is lined with quarries. One of these, at the junction, and a mecca for geology students, is where De la Beche, early in the last century, first identified the Carboniferous-Jurassic unconformity. The line of an old tramway can be traced, from Egford at the head of Vallis Vale, towards Hapsford; here an old watermill was converted to crack the stone for the new turnpike roads. Later the quarries and the tramway were extended up the Mells valley to Great Elm and the Tedbury quarry. A little steam engine pulled the line of tipper tricks up to the quarry, and then pushed them back again — a dangerous place to walk !

With the increased demand for stone in the Second World War the tramway was converted to standard gauge so that mainline trucks could reach the quarry, and a cracker, with its attendant dust, was installed at Hapsford. The people of Great Elm complained bitterly that their ceilings were being shaken down by the blasting, and after the War the line was further extended up the hitherto untouched valley to a new quarry at Whatley. In 1973 the line was straightened again and taken under the road, out of the lower valley, at Great Elm. The waste from this new tunnel was dumped in the De la Beche quarry, even though the valley had been made a SSSI of geological importance. Later the Nature Conservancy Council cleared the upper part of the rock face. When Whatley quarry was big enough the cracker was moved there; the valley at Hapsford, no longer a local beauty spot, is now a semi-derelict industrial site and lorry depot.

What has happened to the rest of the valley through all these changes? Old photographs show a field along the bottom of the valley which was once Frome's playground — it had no common land. With quarrying, grazing ceased and the field reverted to scrub; but people still walk and picnic there. There were dippers and crayfish (*Austropotamobius pallipes Lereboullet*) in the river, and giant bellflowers (*Campanula trachelium*). Dippers and a few clumps of bellflower, hidden in the nettles, remain, but the crayfish have gone. American signal crayfish (*Pacifastacus leniusculus*) were introduced; these carried a fungal infection to which native crayfish are susceptible, so they have vanished from the entire river system. Some of the old quarries were filled with the unsaleable fines from the cracker and, like the earlier waste-stone tips, are now well covered with something like the original vegetation, although only coltsfoot (*Tussilago farfara*) is tough enough to break through the coated stone used to consolidate the slope above the river.

The old rail tracks make popular footpaths to Great Elm, but beyond there main-line stone trains make the valley to Whatley unsafe. Wadbury and Mells can be reached up the other valley, though the river must be forded for this to be strictly legal. Tedbury Camp, freed from the threat of quarrying, is leased to the Scouts, and geology students flock to the exposed uncomformity, to chip their samples of worm-borings from the old seabed. Before quarrying started the stream below Whatley ran dry in summer, gurgling down fissures in the rock to replenish the water table. Early quarrying sent down silty water which covered the river-bed with mud and blocked the fissures. Now the water is clear again, and the flow has increased since quarrying upstream extended below the water table. An improvement, perhaps; but at the expense of other valleys whose spring water has been diverted by the quarries.

In 1973 Frome Urban and Rural District Councils considered taking over Vallis Vale from the quarry company as one of the newly-authorised Country Parks, though they had some reservations about liability for accidents on the cliffs. But by 1974, when the new rail link that made the plan possible was completed, the area had been reorganised. Though it was now called 'Mendip', but extending as far south as Street, the new area's councillors were never interested in Vallis Vale.

What would the area be like now, if the plan had gone ahead?

There is no simple answer as to how such areas should be dealt with. Should natural regeneration be the priority, so that future generations can enjoy the things we knew in the past? Should the preservation of species diversity be an end in itself, even if this means excluding the public from some areas? Should public amenity be the aim — encouraging still more people to visit, to pick the wild flowers, and to disturb wildlife with their dogs? If so, how to prevent vandalism and litter, and how to pay for the necessary wardening? Should sites already badly damaged, as at Hapsford, be sacrificed to industry so as to minimise damage to new sites elsewhere? All of these are legitimate viewpoints. Who is to resolve the conflicts between them ?

Industrial Mendip, where lead was mined and processed, resolved its problems in gentler and more leisurely times. When mining ceased the land was just left for rough grazing, or was planted with conifers. Now these areas, particularly Priddy Mineries, can be matched nowhere else on Mendip, although the flora and fauna are nothing like those before mining began (Plate 7). The Mineries are now both an SSSI and a Nature Reserve, popular with walkers and picnickers and (with help from the Forestry Commission and the exclusion of bikers) able, so far, to

Plate 5: *Quarry sump in Torr Quarry, East Mendip. Groundwater entering the sump is pumped out of the quarry to an adjacent stream.* (Courtesy of Peter Smart).

Plate 6: *Basalt shingle deposit in Iceland. Basalt lavas from Iceland may replace limestone for aggregate use. They should be cheap to produce, easy to ship and are a renewable resource.* (Courtesy of Willie Stanton).

Plate 7: *The Nature Reserve at Priddy Mineries. Flora and fauna are nothing like those before mining began.* (Courtesy of Eunice Overend).

Plate 8: *Wych Elm Stools with Bluebell, Mercury and Wood Spurge in Asham Wood.* (Courtesy of Eunice Overend).

sustain the pressure.

The original oak/ash forest was probably cleared in Neolithic times; the farmers may have lived by the stream above St Cuthbert's Swallet (ST 543504), and then moved on when fertility declined. The moorland which developed on the hill has remained, but the water dammed to wash the lead ore has completely changed the valley — together with the mounds of mud from the buddle-pits where washing and sorting took place, and the mountains of black, glassy slag. The silted ponds are full of new marsh plants — tussock sedge (*Carex paniculata*), marsh orchid (*Dactylorhiza praetermissa*) , marsh fern (*Thelypteris palustris*), marsh pennywort (*Hydrocotyle vulgaris*), lesser spearwort (*Ranunculus flammula*), cotton grass (*Eriophorum angustifolium*) — among the sphagnum moss. Adders and lizards bask in the drier places; swallows roost in the reeds as they gather for migration, and starlings in winter; dragonflies of many species breed in the pools. The slag heaps are slowly being covered by lichens, with sea campion (*Silene uniflora*) which is otherwise only found inland on mountain tops, and two other flowers which are found also on the old lead mines in Derbyshire — spring sandwort (*Minuartia verna*) and a pennycress (*Thlaspi caerulescens*). Across the road in Chewton Warren, the 'gruffy ground', the grooves where galena (lead ore) has been extracted, has been planted with conifers. Many of these are stunted, and there are bare places where nothing will grow because the ground is so contaminated with lead and zinc. Yet, in between are sheets of red fescue grass (*Festuca rubra*) which has developed a local, lead-tolerant race; other plants must be doing the same.

Altogether a unique asemblage, but until quite recently it was taken for granted that the earth was there to be made use of by man, and no one questioned the loss of woodland or heathland. Now we begin to value every bit that remains — and there are few enough of some of them. Yet change is sometimes beneficial — disturbance, management and occasional destruction may be needed if areas like Mendip are to continue to support the diversity of species that can be found there at present.

Asham Wood (Plate 8) *is* a place that should be valued, the last surviving bit of the woodland that once covered Mendip. In the past it has been managed by coppicing and timber extraction, but never clear-felled and replanted.

Thus its ground flora remains intact, with all the expected woodland rarities, including columbine (*Aquilegia vulgaris*) , lily of the valley and even Welsh poppy. It became one of the first SSSIs; yet nearly one quarter of its 200 hectares has since been damaged or destroyed.

I was first taken to Asham before the War, and remember vividly the autumn crocus ('naked ladies' is the local name, lying pale and purple with the cold in the wet grass) in the meadow at Dead Woman's Bottom, where the quarry entrance now is. Later we went in from the north to see the wild daffodils, before the gypsies stripped them, and to collect scarlet moss cups (*Sarcoscypha coccinea*) for winter decoration. We discovered the Devil's Coach Road in the valley, the route later replaced by the turnpike 'Mendip Motorway', and unsuccessfully tried to follow the stream as it disappeared into a muddy subsidence (ST 701459) at the entrance to the wood, to find the cave system below.

The stream from Downhead Common is taken by the swallet near the road, but a pipe the length of the valley took water to a row of cottages at Dead Woman's Bottom; now only badgers use the empty pipe through the wood. The level top of the wood was an easy place to get lost without sun or wind as a guide — I once found my way out by the sound of Chantry church bell. The woods at Hele Ladder were coppiced in the 1950s and the light brought everything into flower the following year. Hele Ladder, opposite the muddy scramble course at Leighton, is an old pack-horse route up to Mendip.

When the Cranmore estate was broken up the woods came up for sale, and after being developed privately they were bought by a major quarrying company. Shortly after the original sale the Nature Conservancy offered to buy part of the land as an SSSI, but was refused. At that time it was easy to obtain planning permission for quarrying, the SSSI designation gave no protection, and almost the whole wood was included within the line of the infamous Interim Development Order, which would cost too much to rescind, and which is still a threat.

Not all of the wood is limestone; the northern edge is gritstone, with a band of soft shale next to it. Very soon a side-valley running northward in the shale was being used as Frome's rubbish tip. Frome then had a plastics factory, and the waste was burnt on the tip, creating continuous clouds of black smoke, causing great annoyance.

Eventually another area south of Frome was brought into use (incidentally a site of archaelogical importance). The Asham tip was then covered with quarry waste, but has still not been successfully recolonised by woodland plants — though whether this is due to the nature of the covering, or what is underneath, is uncertain. One small gain; the top of the valley, dammed by the tip, produced a small pool, still full of drowned trees, which provides the only high-level water supply in the wood.

In 1968 an application was made by a neighbouring quarry company to extract gritsone; some other companies sank boreholes to see what competing resources were available. At the same time the company owning Asham agreed to lease the northern edge of the wood to the Somerset Trust for Nature Conservation as a reserve, with the tacit understanding that gritstone quarrying and new works in the northern valley would not be opposed. In the end permission was refused, and the other companies found too much waste between the beds of stone for quarrying to be worthwhile.

I marked out the area to be leased as a reserve. It included part of the coach-road valley below Downhead and a narrow strip around the western edge of the wood, wide enough to screen any future workings. Yet all but the tip of Tunscombe Bottom (ST 702453), at the southern end, was refused, although the whole valley had been requested for inclusion because of its particularly rich plant assemblage. In the event, if both quarry companies had followed up their options the reserve could, in places, have been only 5 metres wide, and with a 30 metre drop on either side.

It was while marking the reserve that I saw the first muntjac; roe deer had recolonised the woods some 10 years earlier. There were badgers both within and outside the reserve (although a polecat was probably an escaped polecat-ferret). Daffodils, autumn crocus, herb paris, wood vetch (*Vicia sylvatica*), foxgloves (*Digitalis purpurea*) and columbines grew within the reserve, also adder's-tongue fern (*Ophioglossum vulgatum*) and a hybrid geum swarm (*Geum X intermedium*), but not lily of the valley (which we hopefully tried to transplant from the Hele Ladder end), nor Welsh poppy nor the small-leaved lime. Foxgloves, though lime-haters, grow in patches of leached soil in the top of the wood. Since then the reserve has been managed by coppicing (despite its attracting the deer, who find the new shoots a honeypot) to produce a variety of light and shade which both flowers and insects enjoy.

Quarrying continued in the main valley, filling Chantry lake just below with mudbanks of dust. More damaging, oil leaked for many years from an undrained fuel-tank buried in a tip in the quarry opposite. Both problems have now ended and the lake, though reduced in area by the willow scrub on the mudbanks, has begun to recover. Complaints of heavy lorries with their dust and noise led to the suggestion for a conveyor belt to join the railway near Cranmore. This would have damaged Leighton Hanging, with its limes, whitebeams and cherries, but fortunately the plan fell through because of the presence of the motorcycle scramble course.

A dispute, still not fully resolved, then arose as to exactly how much of Asham Wood had been given permission for limestone extraction. Another company working the quarry attempted to pre-empt the judgement by clearing a large part of the wood and removing the overburden to dump on a further area of the wood, thereby betraying their disregard for conservation. The land then changed hands yet again, work ended, and the exposed rock, interesting geologically, is now being recolonised by birch and buddleia — a long way from the prehistoric forest that was on the site only 50 years ago. With luck it may not now be needed for extraction of stone; yet there is always the threat, if the present demand continues, that it will become a reserve area for the future.

This raises the key question, can the present demand for aggregates, let alone the higher demands projected for the future, continue to be satisfied? Common sense in a finite world says no; production must, at some time, begin to decline, either slowly or catastrophically. Demand is driven, in part at least, by increasing affluence (though not of everyone, itself an unstable situation) and partly by increasing population. There is an alarming resemblance between the graphs in Figures 19 and 20 and other population graphs, from algae to locusts and lemmings, in which the second half is a mirror image of the first. When shall we reach the peak ?

When the decline does come, reclaiming abandoned quarries will be far down the list of priorities, so whatever is necessary must be put in hand now, while there are still resources to support it. True, in a thousand years time the vast quarry faces may become as scenic as Cheddar Gorge; but people find it hard to think beyond their grandchildren's day, and want action now to repair the visible devastation. As a minimum, rock faces must be made safe from slides (as safe as limestone can ever be); holes that will fill with water as soon as pumping ceases should be cleared of rubbish; and tipping should be organised to provide access banks and shallows. So any future use will be accommodated, and past mistakes not perpetuated.

What are the options, and where do the priorities lie? Conservation? Public amenity? Cash return? None of these is exclusive; there is room for a range of options, but there may well be conflict over particular sites. Thus there is a very strong case for conservation at Asham Wood; yet the public would like unlimited access, and one can well imagine a leisure development company seeing this as a profitable site for expensive outdoor pursuits.

If conservation were the main objective the remaining woodland, while cherished, would need informed management to maintain its diversity. The stripped limestone would provide a new habitat, and a visible demonstration of natural succession. Unrestricted public access could cause damage, but access might be limited, as at present, by the distance and difficulty of reaching the site, which only dedicated walkers and naturalists would be likely to penetrate. On the other hand a leisure company might see it as the ideal place for war-games and off-road driving, both of which would undoubtedly cause unacceptable disturbance and damage.

Most visitors to the countryside come from the town; they like car parks with spaced-out bays for picnicking, preferably with a good view. Some will venture a little way around signposted trails, and will read information boards and trail leaflets. A growing minority of people now reads maps and will explore along public footpaths. Mendip, and its abandoned quarries, can provide for all of these. Judicious tipping and planting can produce inconspicuous parking with occasional visitors' centres and camping sites on the bare floor of the quarry. All this assumes, of course, that affluent society, like the demand for aggregates, will continue to grow; but so, too, will its non-affluent members, many of whom seem compelled to destroy anything the 'other side' values. Toilets and information boards are targets, bikes roar along footpaths. 'Travellers' occupy camp sites, so that wardening becomes policing, a separate skill from the sensitive management of specialised habitats. In addition to the initial outlay, picnic areas must be kept tidy and paths cleared. People traditionally dislike paying for access to the countryside — though they are willing to do so for country sports such as golf, fishing and shooting. Unless it is linked to such money-making projects, how can the use of land for public amenity, or even conservation, be financed to safeguard it in perpetuity?

Modern quarrying inevitably produces huge scars which the public wants to see hidden as quickly as possible — leaving it to nature is much too slow. The quarry companies, more attentive to public opinion since the 1968 gritstone application was refused, have turned to landscaping as the answer. There is plenty of scope through well-managed tipping, but what should then be planted? Restoring a site to its original state would be impossible, though limited areas with the right slope and aspect could be planted to match and mimic what remains. Purists might demand that only native species should be used, preferably grown from Mendip seed, but this would be a counsel of perfection. Local seed is not available, and alien species are with us already — sycamore, buddleia and all the conifers. Most of the extensive broad-leaved woodland planting in recent years is from continental stock, for example the hawthorn of new roadside hedges is in leaf three weeks earlier than the rest. Each area develops its own adapted varieties, such as the lead-tolerant plants on Mendip. Moving them around at random will result in genetic contamination and loss of diversity. Introducing new aliens needs considerable care. Russian vine (*Fallopia baldschuanica*) does not set seed, or creep underground; yet who, looking from the Quantocks, can tell whether it, or Old Man's beard(*Clematis vitalba*) is the creeper that is greening the Batts Combe scars? In contrast the related Japanese knotweed (*Fallopia japonica*) creeps so aggressively that there is an eradication programme against it in Wiltshire. The seeds of wild flowers now being sprayed on roadside verges and grown in wild gardens are also mostly of continental origin. Care is needed to avoid planting this contaminated seed anywhere near places where there is a chance of recolonisation from neighbouring undisturbed sites. Contamination of another sort can be even more dangerous. A disease carried by an alien which is not susceptible to it can eliminate a native species, as happened with the crayfish. Their numbers were normal until the disease struck; species with small numbers or fragmented populations are even more vulnerable — the whole local population of greater horseshoe bats, nationally threatened with extinction, could have been exterminated had the vandals' fire been by day. Changes in woodland management have reduced dormouse populations to danger levels nationaly, though they still live in Mendip's old woods.

For a long time the quarrying industry gave no thought to what it was leaving behind, expecting nature to cover huge new areas of dereliction as rapidly as it had the little hollows of earlier quarrying. Now the new landscaping can ensure that our grandchildren will not find the Mendip quarry-scars an eyesore, and the disused quarries themselves may become their playground — but only if all the quarry companies play their part and keep the restoration up-to-date as each area is worked out. There may be less concern about covering deep reserves, which has inhibited such plans in the past, if increased supplies of aggregate become available from the new coastal super-quarries. But not all quarry companies have future landscape and conservation in mind, as the destruction in Asham Wood demonstrated, and continual public pressure through planning constraints will be needed, to give the Mendips a chance of regaining their old beauty.

But landscaping is not conservation. It cannot afford to wait for natural regeneration or avoid introducing species which, spreading, may upset finely-balanced ecosystems.

Yet have we not a duty to pass on to our grandchildren as rich a world as we ourselves received? Those who think in terms of stewardship, and have seen the havoc of the last 50 years, fear for the next. They would like to see an end to quarrying before more irreparable harm is done.

In 1940 no one could have guessed that the next 50 years would see more change than the last 5,000, and we are in no better position now to judge where technology is leading us. We must cherish what remains on Mendip, both beauty and diversity, against all eventualities until, as must happen one day, the dream of sustainable growth shatters itself against the reality of a finite world.

REFERENCES

Alderman, D.J. 1992. *Crayfish Plague in Great Britain, the First Twelve Years.* MAFF, British Crown Copyright.

Aston, M. and Burrow, I., Eds 1982. *The Archaeology of Somerset.* Somerset County Council.

Harris, S. Ed. *British Mammals, Past, Present and Future.* Mammal Society.

ACKNOWLEDGEMENTS

Peter F. Hunt, International Orchid Registrar, for help with flowers.

John White, Dendrologist, Forestry Commission, for help with trees.

ARC Southern, for updating the Asham story.

LIMESTONE QUARRYING: THE DEBATE

Frank Raymond,
Christmas Common, Watlington, Oxfordshire

This was a remarkable meeting which, instead of becoming bogged down solely in local issues, first gave particular attention to the question of the demand for aggregates at the national level, which must precede the more local questions of where, and on what scale, aggregates should be extracted. National demand forecasts are the responsibility of the Department of the Environment, and are published at intervals in the form of Mineral Planning Guidance Note 6 (MPG6). Regional Aggregate Working Parties (RAWP) are then required to establish landbanks 'sufficient to meet this forecast demand in full'. The problem, as Richard Moon had noted, is that the Working Parties also have to negotiate the allocation of this demand between regions, with any shortfall in one region having to be made up by other regions; but they are not expected to question the projected demand for aggregates at the national level.

David Tidmarsh described the way in which these national forecasts are drawn up. Essentially the consultants, ECOTEC and Cambridge Econometrics, have assumed that economic activity (GDP) will increase at least as fast over the next 20 years as it has over the last 20 years; that construction activity will increase at a somewhat greater rate than GDP; and that the use of aggregates by the construction industry will grow even faster than this, because each £1,000 of construction investment will consume more aggregates than in the past. The net result is that the draft consultation document for MPG6, issued in January 1993, predicted a sharp increase in demand for aggregates, from 230M tonnes in 1992 to 'between 370 and 440M tonnes in 2011'; this compares with the highest previous demand, of 270M tonnes, in 1989.

Perhaps not everyone at the seminar would have gone as far as Roger Martin, of the Wildlife Trust, in suggesting that an appropriate acronym for the data on which MPG6 is based would be GIGO (Garbage In Gospel Out); but many delegates did query the assumptions underlying these demand projections; the economic assumptions — that both construction and road-building activity will increase over the next 20 years at an exponential rate — and the environmental assumptions — that neither the increased construction activity, nor the resulting greater demand for quarried aggregates, will have unacceptable environmental consequences. Certainly the comment in para 4.11 of the consultation document, that 'the (environmental) concerns expressed are more subjective than objective' does suggest that the potential for damage, clearly described in the papers by Willie Stanton and Eunice Overend, may have been too readily dismissed by the Department of the Environment — and also by the quarrying industry itself, which 'considers that the environmental implications of meeting the projected level of demand have been overstated, with undue emphasis placed on the views of a minority' (para 3.2). Certainly one of the stated objectives of minerals policy (para 7.10, 'to avoid sterilisation of mineral resources') would seem to discourage any new site which might have potential for quarrying being designated as an SSSI.

No one at the seminar questioned David Tidmarsh's statement that society will continue to demand improved provision of housing, schools, hospitals, roads, offices and factories. What was questioned was the way in which the future level of this provision, and the consequential levels of construction activity and demand for aggregates, have been assessed. Most of those who intervened considered that the resulting projections are both unrealistic and unsustainable — as Roger Martin noted, the UK has used more than 7 billion tonnes of aggregates in the 90 years since 1900; are we really likely to use the same quantity over the next 20 years? Yet under the present planning system, once a projected level of demand has been confirmed the local minerals authorities must designate enough land to ensure that this level of demand can be satisfied; as Richard Dixon (FoE) observed, the projections in effect then become self-fulfilling.

Thus the debate stressed the urgent need for a critical re-examination of the estimates of future aggregate demand, and in particular of the projected demand for road construction, which currently accounts for one third of aggregates use in the UK. David Tidmarsh made the point that, at present, 80% of this is used for repair of existing roads (the 'cones' jobs), and only 20% for construction of new roads, although data from the trade association BACMI do indicate a rather higher figure. Certainly this proportion would increase markedly if recently announced plans are implemented. Thus the Department of Transport report, 'Trunk Roads in England into the 1990s', proposed the construction of 24,000 km of new road lanes by the end of the century. This would require 1800 million tonnes of aggregates over the 10-year period (equivalent to 70% of current aggregates output), compared with only 500 million tonnes if road-building continued at the same (considerable) rate as in the late 1980s (CPRE, 'Driven to Dig'; 1993). The planned increase in road-building is thus one of the main reasons for the projected near-doubling in the demand for aggregates, with particular potential impact on Somerset.

Fortunately, though for reasons quite unrelated to the risk of environmental damage, the Treasury seems unlikely fully to fund this higher rate of road building. Similarly the financial markets are unlikely to support a repeat of the speculative building construction boom of the 1980s, which appears to be implicit in the projected demand for aggregates. Yet doubt was expressed that there will be any significant reduction, in the forthcoming revision of MPG6, from the 7,000 million tonnes projected demand for aggregates over the next 20 years. A more realistic scenario may have to wait until 'sustainability' assumes a more central focus in official policy. But this means that, in the immediate future, RAWP will have to continue to add to their planned landbanks, so as to meet the increased demand for aggregates that is currently projected — and in the process cast still further 'planning blight' on areas such as the Mendips.

The seminar also gave attention to a further important objective, of increasing the proportion of 'secondary' aggregates in the total aggregates that are used. As Ramous Gallois had noted, there is some scope for increasing the use of demolition materials, of which only half the present 24 million tonnes produced annually are used; but the main target must be the huge amounts of other potential materials that are available, including 600 million tonnes of china clay waste and 2,000 million tonnes of mine waste. A report by Arup Partners had examined the possible use of such secondary aggregates, and had identified a number of reasons why they are not at present used; partly because they are often in the wrong place; partly because they are often less suitable for construction than primary aggregates; but mainly because the low cost of primary aggregates provides little incentive for the construction industry to use alternative materials (though we were also told that some residents in Scotland and Wales have objected to proposals to remove local slag heaps and slate waste because this would 'damage their environment').

Clearly there are technical limitations to the use of waste materials. Thus David Tidmarsh noted that, while road contracts in Germany specify that 25% of the road sub-base must be of recycled waste, this may not give a corresponding reduction in the use of primary aggregates because the depth of the sub-base may have to be increased. However to date there has been little interest in the greater use of secondary aggregates in the UK, and this is only likely to happen if there is a significant rise in the cost of primary aggregates. Several speakers proposed that this should be brought about by imposing a levy on primary aggregates. Humphrey Temperley suggested that, if such a levy were introduced, it should initially be set at a fairly low level, and increased incrementally; but most delegates considered that, to be effective, a levy would have to be large enough to have an immediate impact on construction costs, and so on demand for primary aggregates. Martin Milmore noted that there is already a small tax on quarry extraction, and suggested that the industry would not oppose a further environmental levy (for, as David Tidmarsh pointed out, this would be paid for by the users, and not by the quarry operators!). But although Arup had calculated that a 30% levy would reduce demand for aggregates by 50 million tonnes, Oliver Tickell, in the current *New Scientist*, had suggested that a levy of £5 per tonne would raise the cost of an average house by only

£250; would this be enough to lead to less aggregates being used in housebuilding?

However there was general support for the principle of a 'polluter pays' levy on aggregates — and unanimous agreement that, if such a levy were introduced, the proceeds should not go to the Exchequer, because government pays for a major part of UK construction activity, so that the receipts from any levy would then merely be recycled. One suggestion, that the proceeds should go to quarry operators to pay for the restitution of quarry sites was not generally supported, because it was considered that restitution should be a condition of the quarrying licence, and should already be included in the sale price of the aggregate (though it was accepted that the conditions attached to some earlier licences, as at Batts Combe, had been quite inadequate). There was more support for a number of other proposals, though with the recognition that some of them would be opposed by the Treasury because they would imply 'hypothecation' of funds. Thus it was suggested that the levy should be paid to the appropriate county council, to support environmental measures outside the immediate area covered by quarrying licences, to improve the tourist potential of often scenic areas, and to create new employment opportunities as an alternative to employment in the quarrying industry. There was also much support for the proposal that part of any levy should be used to fund research aimed at increasing the use of secondary aggregates (such research had already been done on a small scale in Cornwall), with the best-qualified UK centres to carry out such research being the Building Research and Road Research Laboratories. Humphrey Temperley also suggested that part of the proceeds from a levy might be needed to indemnify users, under 'product liability', for occasional failures when secondary aggregates are used.

Both measures — increased use of secondary aggregates, and a levy on primary aggregates — should lead to a reduced demand for primary aggregates, and so to reduced quarrying activity. Willie Stanton had also proposed that quarrying in sensitive areas such as the Mendips should be further reduced by sourcing more of the aggregates that are used in the UK from alternative, less environmentally sensitive areas. These might include coastal superquarries in Scotland and Norway, and lava and gravel deposits such

as those he had identified in Iceland. But, as Humphrey Temperley had reminded us, while there might be scope for some increase in supply from these sources, there would be considerable opposition in Scotland to anything like the 30M tonnes per year output from superquarries, proposed by Savory (Quarry Management 1991) — and in Iceland to the proposal to transfer part of that island to South East England!

Changes in aggregate sourcing would also have other consequences; certainly any significant increase in coastal quarrying would require the construction of major new port facilities, and the upgrading of transport links from ports to construction sites, with considerable economic and environmental costs. Increased reliance on foreign imports would also have undesirable impacts on both the UK balance of trade and on employment — though it was noted that the present run-down of the mining industry did not indicate that either employment or balance of payments were currently of high priority.

The overall conclusion was that there could, and should, be a significant reduction in the future demand for aggregates from the Mendips from that currently required by MPG6. As Humphrey Temperley had shown, approval for quarrying, either full or outline, had already been granted on an area of the Mendips containing some 600 million tonnes of Carboniferous limestone — sufficient for quarrying to continue for 40 years at the current rate of extraction of 12-15M tonnes per year. It was accepted that this would cause further environmental damage, and every attempt should be made to minimise this by selection of sites, and by imposing more stringent operating and restitution conditions for quarrying. What was not acceptable was the requirement in the MPG6 consultation document that the annual rate of extraction of aggregates from the Mendips should be increased to 32M tonnes per year; at that rate the present landbank would last for only 16 years, and large new areas of the Mendips would have to be licensed for mineral extraction. It was argued that this should present no real problem, for David Tidmarsh had made the point that the quarrying industry at present has permission to operate on an area of only 1 square mile. However, as Ramous Gallois and Peter Smart had shown, only a fraction of the total area of the Mendips contains limestone suitable for quarrying — and much of the area that is not yet licensed is either designated as AONB or SSSI, is close to settlements, or is of key water-supply importance. It is for this reason that the RAWP had concluded that little additional area can be allocated for future mineral extraction without unacceptable risk of environmental damage.

A number of delegates argued that this analysis seemed to suggest that, while the Mendips cannot cope with any increase in quarrying activity, it can probably continue to live with the present rate of extraction; this led to a lively debate.

For while many of those who spoke on this subject considered that the curent rate of environmental damage was already unacceptable, and that quarrying activity should be reduced, it was clear that not everyone considered that quarrying, and in particular abandoned quarries, are necessarily a blot on the landscape. Thus George Gamble questioned whether quarrying, certainly at current levels, had damaged the tourist potential of the Mendips to the extent suggested by Willie Stanton, while Eunice Overend observed that some old quarry sites, with their characteristic limestone flora, are very attractive. It was clear, however, that the main concern was with the potential impact of the newer large quarries, particularly in East Mendip. It was suggested that these might later be landscaped as country parks; but this objective would have to be defined right from the start of quarrying, and would certainly demand stricter planning conditions than at present apply, in particular in relation to the stabilisation of terraces and the management of the lakes formed within deep quarries. David Tidmarsh suggested that these lakes could provide useful new water storage capacity — though, as Willie Stanton noted, this might require pumping lower-grade water from rivers while the same area, left unquarried, would provide much greater, high quality, water storage capacity.

Most delegates almost certainly agreed with the observation by John Franklin that it was the speed of expansion of quarrying activity in the 1980s, in particular in East Mendip, that had most focused attention on the environmental damage that was being caused, and on the need for stricter control on these operations. For, as

Humphrey Temperley noted, many existing licences did not impose adequate control, while the cost of 'buying out' leases already granted was quite unsustainable — the £250,000 paid out in the early 1960s to prevent a damaging extension of quarrying activity on Crook's Peak, on West Mendip, would be nearer £1 million today.

David Tidmarsh suggested that one way of approaching this problem would be through a more flexible planning system, which would allow sites now considered to be unsuitable to be traded off against less sensitive new areas. The discussion indicated that this would apply in particular to quarry operations that might damage water supplies (at present possibly more of a risk to local water supply, as had already happened at Frome, than to the Mendip catchment as a whole); to sites close to towns and villages (though with some disagreement apparent between the present and past chairmen of Leigh-on-Mendip Parish Council); and to sites, already identified as AONBs and SSSIs, which are at the heart of the natural beauty of the Mendip Hills.

For to seek a cessation of quarrying in the Mendips was quite unrealistic. Society will continue to need new roads and new houses, and the Mendips will be expected to contribute to the supply of aggregates needed to build those roads and houses. Yet there was clearly an over-riding concern among the delegates at the threat of what a *Farming News* reporter graphically described as 'a canyon five miles long and hundreds of feet deep across the most scenic parts of the Mendips.' To prevent this threat becoming a reality there was wide agreement that there should, at the very least, be no increase from the present level of limestone quarrying in the Mendips and that, whatever the scale of quarrying, operating conditions should be tightened so as to minimise the risk of environmental damage.

Thus the 'conflict of interest' in the title of the seminar emerged, not as a conflict between 'them' and 'us', but as the conflict within each of us between the desire for 'progress' and the desire for 'environmental sustainability'. This will require compromise; the necessary balance within that compromise will provide a key subject for debate — and for decision — as we approach the twenty-first century.